Dr Pixie's
Baby and Toddler
Meal Planner

igloobooks

To Mitch, a brilliant dad and a best friend

Published in 2016
by Igloo Books Ltd
Cottage Farm
Sywell
NN6 0BJ
www.igloobooks.com

LEO002 0516
2 4 6 8 10 9 7 5 3 1
ISBN 978-1-78440-198-6

Cover designed by Nicholas Gage
Interiors designed by Charles Wood-Penn
Edited by Vicky Taylor

Cover © Anastasia Veldman / Alamy Stock Photo

Printed and manufactured in China

"Nothing goes exactly to plan where kids are concerned, but if you follow a few simple guidelines, you really can't go too wrong."

Contents

❄ When you see this symbol, it means this recipe is suitable for home freezing.

Foreword

As a doctor you would think I would have known everything there was to know when it came to the nutritional requirements of kids. But, like many parents, I found myself abruptly at the weaning stage with my daughter without ever having given a second thought as to how and when I was going to wean. I felt my way through the first stages and sneakily followed other people's leads, picking out the best bits from their advice and slowly finding my feet.

The transition from mush to mash was interesting. Despite being proficient in child resuscitation, I always checked and double-checked everything for lumps, bumps and bones. Like most first-time parents I mistook gagging for choking and was slow to upgrade to actual solids. I was also a bit obsessed with temperatures and fearful of freezing food. When I finally sussed that my child could happily pick up a piece of carrot and munch it I wondered what all the fuss had been about. She was more than able. I was doing alright.

But then her fussy eating phase began. What had I done wrong? Nothing, it seems! The fussy phase appears to be somewhat of a rite of passage. The little madam was simply telling me 'I have landed and from now on I rule the roost'. It took me a while to realize that what might be flavour of the month one night in terms of food might become the enemy by the following morning. I soon learnt to limit drinks and resist the temptation for comfort milk if I was to get her to taste any of my culinary delights. At the start I cooked up all kinds of complex concoctions but ultimately I learnt kids want it kept simple. I also learnt the hard way that if they expect it now, that doesn't mean they will sit and wait quietly for 20 minutes while you whisk something up. Timing is everything and a tired, hungry child... well that is something else!

Being a hugely disorganized individual, I soon learnt if you aren't prepped for feeding time at the zoo the day is going to be painful. There is what I like to call 'the fine line' between discontent and utter meltdown. To cater for this I always had a few quick and easy food fixes up my sleeve. It's not against the law to eat cold food or cereal for supper, after all. Neither is it bad parenting to resort to a jar of food on occasion. It is also important to swallow one's pride if the food you have slaved over gets flung back in your face. Pick it up, deal with it and move on. There is no place for emotion!

I, like my child, toddled my way through the various feeding phases. Like her, I surpassed myself when I met some milestones but fell behind at others. I always kept the wise words of my mother in the back of my mind: 'Children eat when they are hungry. Relax.' How right she was!

Dr Pixie McKenna

"Children eat
when they
are hungry.
Relax."

Introduction

"Knowing what to expect is half the battle when making the move to solids."

Parenting is sometimes like a competitive sport and so far you will have rated yourself against other parents on so many levels. It almost seems natural to race to be the first to wean. Don't subscribe to it, you are not against the clock! Adding complementary foods to your child's diet is a major developmental milestone. Don't rush it or you will miss the point of it!

First and foremost, you need to be prepared. The first step is buying the kit – never wean without the correct equipment! Plastic spoons are essential – small enough for a baby's mouth, bright enough to look interesting. A high chair is also essential as your baby then knows she has her own personal space in which she can make her own mess – plus, she will be safely restrained. If she is self-feeding, buy a high chair with a built-in tray, then she can just take food from this. It's useful to buy a mat to go under the chair if you want to save your floor.

Next, think carefully about where baby is going to sit at the table. What is in her line of fire? Ensure the seating plan puts her where she can do the least damage if she lets fly with her food! If you are starting with purées, food should be served in plastic bowls or plates with rims. Start her using a cup as soon as you can, which will get her used to sipping not sucking and makes it easier to get her off the bottle. Remember, if you choose to wean before six months you must sterilize all the utensils as you would your baby's bottles.

Finally, pick a time. Just because bambino hits the 26-week mark on a Monday doesn't mean it's marks, set, wean. Choose a time when you know you are going to be able to do it in a calm and relaxed manner.

For fridge storage and batch freezing, plastic storage tubs are ideal. For small babies it is possible to freeze feeds in ice cube trays and defrost as needed. Buy some labels so you know what's what and when it was made. Everything looks the same when it's frozen and you don't want to defrost a dinner to discover it's a dessert! Equally, you don't want to guesstimate how long something has been lurking in the fridge; if in doubt throw it out. While it is wonderful to be a domestic goddess and cook everything from scratch, don't set your standards too high. Ready-made purées and packet foods do your baby no harm, just try not to make a habit of it. The real deal provides more nutritional value and costs less, but does create mess. Different ready-made brands have different textures and stages of lumpiness, so find one you like and stick to it.

The transition to solids is a big one. Previously you only had to worry about preparing or expressing a bottle or putting your baby to the breast. Now, feeding takes up more of your time and there is more mess. Allow for this and factor it in to your daily routine. I have lost count of the number of times I have ended up splattered in green slush just before I was about to head out to work. The dress code for feeding children should read 'dress for extreme mess'. I have gone so far as to wear a hair net on occasion! It's a messy messy sport!

While to date most of the feeding role may have fallen on mum if baby was exclusively breast fed, weaning makes it a family affair. It is a great opportunity for dads, carers and siblings to bond with the little one and be more involved in her care. It is also a good opportunity for mum to take a step back. Dads can be especially helpful where nappies are concerned! Pre-solids nappies might not be pleasant but they take on a whole new meaning once solids come on board. Breast-fed poo is generally a mustard- or chicken korma-coloured mush. Formula-fed babies produce poo that looks like peanut butter. When first foods are introduced, however, the stool changes, it thickens in consistency, darkens in colour and takes on a strong aroma. Yes, you got it, it stinks! The frequency of motions may change with the change in diet – that's normal. You might also notice telltale signs of what baby has eaten, like sweetcorn lurking in the stool. Don't panic, this is all part of the process.

This book aims to support you with your weaning journey by providing you with expert information and the latest government guidance, but ultimately many of the decisions you need to make will just require you to listen to your baby. Familiarizing yourself with this and using the meal planners and recipes will hopefully help you feel more relaxed about weaning your baby – knowing what to expect is half the battle when making the move to solids. It's a huge step in the development of your baby so try to see it as a milestone rather than a phase she has to pass through. Enjoy it. Some days will be great and others will end in disaster, but keep in mind tomorrow is always another day.

Which weaning method to use

After six months on the fast-track baby-managing course you probably now feel you have it sussed? As with every step on the developmental milestone chart, once you have conquered one, another crops up to challenge you! Welcome to the world of weaning. Let's firstly clear something up: by weaning I mean the transition from milk to purée. Americans use the term slightly differently, so to them weaning means being weaned off the breast. Weaning shouldn't be seen as a time when your little one gives up milk, but rather a time when he explores and ingests solids. At the start, they seem to do more of the former than the latter!

When to wean

The first contentious and confusing issue with weaning is when to do it. International guidelines set out by the World Health Organisation are pretty clear, stating six months, but if you look back to pre-2001 four to six months was considered fine. As a doctor, I would say hold on until the 26-week mark, your baby isn't missing out on anything he can't get from the breast or a bottle in the first six months. He has a whole life of solids ahead of him so don't force the issue too early. If you give in and wean earlier, it's not the end of the world but you do need to brace yourself for some digestive upset. Don't feel judged or bullied in your choice. Remember, mother knows best, though if you don't know or are in any way confused, don't be afraid to ask! If you do decide to start weaning earlier than the 26-week deadline, just make sure baby has hit 17 weeks. Solids are definitely not advised before this date.

Weaning methods

The next confusing issue is which type of weaning method do you follow? What, there are two? I was surprised to learn this when I had my daughter! I had assumed once weaning began, so too did your relationship with the blender. Well, I was behind the times. Around 2006 the baby-led weaning movement began, but that was long after my paediatric training. There are pros and cons to each method, as I discovered.

Advantages of traditional weaning	Disadvantages of traditional weaning
Preparing meals in advance is easy as you can batch cook and freeze purées	It is easy to overfeed your baby
It is easy to measure how much your baby has eaten	A lot of time can be spent preparing purées
It is less messy than other methods	Your baby is usually eating something different from the rest of the family
It teaches your baby how to use utensils from the start	Your baby is not learning about individual foods, tastes and textures when they are blended together
It ensures that iron-rich foods are eaten easily	

Traditional weaning

Traditional weaning starts with 'spoon feeding'. Initially, food is puréed, then gradually the consistency given gets lumpier as you move to mashed meals. Then you graduate to minced consistency or chopped-up food with the ultimate aim of family food by 12 months. Finger foods tend to be introduced around the seven months stage, starting with soft ones then progressing to harder ones. With traditional weaning there's a lot of prep and your baby doesn't graze on regular family food unless it has been pulped. The trajectory to lumpy textures and then true food is nonetheless fairly easy and less messy as you accelerate through the stages.

Baby-led weaning

Baby-led weaning is essentially the introduction of solid foods without the need to purée or spoon feed. It's a concept that has been gaining popularity over the last decade and for some parents and babies, it's a great choice. At six months a baby can usually sit up unsupported and he can reach and grasp. His hand–eye co-ordination is such that he can bring things to his mouth after he has picked them up from a flat surface. It seems nature has already given him all the tools he needs to tackle food, so going straight to formal food and bypassing liquidized dishes does make sense. Parents worry about the choking risk of baby-led weaning but there should not be any greater choking concern in comparison with the traditional method. Babies' gag reflexes become active far further forward in their mouths at this age so food is usually fired back out at you if it's not going down. While your baby may not have teeth, his gums will serve very well in terms of chewing.

Which method is best?

Which method you choose is down to you. Both are merely guides as to how you go about weaning and many parents may decide to pick the best of both methods. Some might want to go old school and stick to structured weaning. Others might like to let baby take the lead. There's no wrong way – the important thing is doing what's right for you and your baby.

Advantages of baby-led weaning	Disadvantages of baby-led weaning
It develops confidence and independence because your baby is feeding himself	It can be very messy
There is less preparation time involved	It can be more difficult to plan for eating out of the home
It allows your baby to explore a variety of colours, tastes and textures	Iron-rich foods are harder for your baby to chew
It develops his hand–eye co-ordination and chewing skills	Sometimes it is difficult to tell how much your baby has eaten
Your baby is more involved in family mealtimes	

What your baby needs

Weaning at six months is a natural developmental step. Your baby can 'sit up' and 'pick up' and is able to put things in her mouth by this stage. She will be curious and keen to interact and mimic because she has seen everybody else enjoy family food. While weaning makes sense because your baby is ready in terms of what she can physically do, it also makes sound nutritional sense. She needs the supplementary energy and nutrients from solids that she simply won't get exclusively from breast or bottle at this stage. For this reason, delaying weaning is not advised – babies should not be fed on the breast or bottle alone beyond six months. Iron deficiency and deficiencies in protein and vitamins A and D can occur in late weaners, though you should continue to give your baby 500–600 ml per day of breast or fortified formula milk in addition to solids. Delaying weaning may also result in your child not being able to adapt to novel foods or even feeding. Biting and chewing movements ultimately assist speech development. Each child is different, however, and as a parent you are the best placed to make the decision for your little one. If in doubt, check with your health-care professional.

Different needs

Premature babies need to be assessed individually in terms of their readiness for solids as each baby is different in terms of their development. Children with cystic fibrosis and other metabolic disorders may need to be weaned earlier than 26 weeks to meet increased calorie demands in these disorders. Babies with specific illnesses may have different nutritional needs as a result of their particular ailment but if this is the case, weaning is normally done with the help of a health-care professional. For the vast majority of little ones, once you hit the 26-week mark, solids should be going on the menu.

Reducing milk feeds

The switch from just mother's milk or formula to solid feeding is not an instant transition. As a parent, don't panic and don't push it – it's a big milestone in your baby's life. In the initial stages she will take very little in terms of calories from her new adventure with solid foods, so the milk requirement may seem to be the same. So, when is the right time to drop a milk feed? Should you cut out the morning or afternoon feed first? This can be decided by you and your baby. You will probably notice that your baby takes less milk in the feed after her breakfast or lunch, depending on how much she eats. Try to make her main meal at lunchtime so that your baby isn't too full after her evening supper; this way she is more likely to be interested in her last milk feed before bed which will help keep her going until the morning. Slowly the amount of milk feeds will reduce. If you are breast-feeding you have to use your instincts to quantify. Some children are milk monsters and need coaxing to reduce their 'fix'!

Food group	Includes	Nutrition	Portions
Starchy foods	Bread, pasta, rice, couscous, noodles and potatoes	Introduce white bread, pasta and rice rather than wholemeal as the fibre in these foods will fill up your baby more quickly and so she may not have room for the other foods she needs	Try to include something from this food group with each meal, ideally 5 servings per day
Fruits and vegetables	Fruits and vegetables	Providing a varied selection of different coloured fruit and vegetables will ensure your baby is getting the phytonutrients she needs	Offer your baby 5 portions of fruits or vegetables each day
Dairy	Milk, yogurt, fromage frais, crème fraiche, soft cheese, hard cheese	Full-fat versions of these foods should be provided until your baby reaches two years old	As your baby reduces her milk feeds it is important to include 3 portions of dairy foods in her daily diet
Proteins	Beef, lamb, pork, chicken, eggs, turkey, white fish, oily fish, beans and pulses	Make sure eggs are well cooked	On average try to offer two portions from this food group each day

First foods

Weaning is your baby's first chance to taste and explore a variety of new foods. As mentioned previously, these first foods do not add much nutritional content to your baby's diet as much of it may end up around his face or on the floor! The gut and immune system need to mature, so ideally waiting for your baby to be six months old is best, otherwise your child may be more prone to infection and allergy. There is no evidence that weaning early turns your child into a super-strong, super-clever human being later in life. However, each child is different – just remember that if you do decide to go off piste, don't dish out solids until he is at least 17 weeks old. Remember also that if you elect to wean before six months, bowls and spoons must be sterilized. For premature babies or babies with other medical problems, seek advice from a health-care professional for each individual case and if you are in any doubt about the developmental readiness of your baby, you should also ask for advice. Sitting, co-ordination and a readiness to swallow are the key milestones when it comes to solid food. If your little one pushes the food back out at you, he may not be ready. Bide your time, otherwise more will end up on the bib than in the baby!

Stage 1

Stage 1 weaning usually starts at 26 weeks. It often begins with smooth purées but at six months many babies may be able to handle food that is slightly lumpier. Baby-led weaning is becoming more common, but if you choose to go the conventional route and pulp and blend, that's fine too.

What to feed your baby

So what kind of things would your little one like on his inaugural journey of taste? You could start with baby rice mixed with breast or formula milk, which is neutral in flavour and lets your baby become accustomed to a texture that is slightly thicker than milk. While he has to date been used to continuous, free-flowing food, don't be tempted to tip the baby rice or any first foods into a bottle as this poses a choking risk. Fruit and veg are also appropriate first foods, or additional first foods in the early weeks. Smooth sweet potato, banana, parsnip, carrot or pear all usually go down a treat. Babies are hardwired to prefer sweet to savoury so start the journey with veg, then vary the veg before you bring on the fruit. Of course, babies can and should have fruit, but reserve it for pudding or after their savoury portion. Don't expect your child to eat copious amounts; exploration is as important as ingestion at this early stage. He won't starve if he doesn't scoff as expected, if he is still on milk feeds.

Self-feeding

Allow your child to self-feed wherever possible. Never add salt or sugar to jazz things up, and just because you don't like something doesn't mean your child won't! If you wish to spoon feed him try to let him come to the spoon, not the other way round. Never ever force a child to eat, it's dangerous. And try to relax. They may be small, but even babies pick up on the attention they get if there is a standoff!

Signs your baby is ready for weaning	Signs that can be mistaken for readiness to wean
Holds his head up and maintains an upright position without support	Chewing fists - your baby may be teething
Starts to watch you eat your food and follows food from the plate to your mouth	Waking in the night – he may be too hot/cold or starting to crawl/walk
Can make a chewing motion. Food is swallowed rather than dribbling out of his mouth	Increasing milk feeds – this could indicate a growth spurt or he may just be thirsty if the weather is hot
Has developed a pincer grasp to hold foods and can move it into his mouth (especially needed for baby-led weaning)	

Introducing texture

At six months baby is usually able to take liquidized food from a spoon either herself or with assistance. She will learn that she needs to move the food from the front of the mouth to the back to allow her to swallow it. It's a different skill set to supping milk! It comes out a lot at the start but in time you will find you are no longer being plastered in purée!

Try not to linger in the liquidized phase for too long. It's time to take the leap from sucking to chewing. Introducing texture means your baby will break down food and work her mouth muscles, enabling her to broaden her nutritional horizons and get a step closer to sharing family foods. Not only this, the activity helps with development of muscles of speech, meaning you could soon be thanked for all your efforts! Parents of early weaners may find they are slower to progress to the next phase, as might late weaners, but again each child is different. If your little one seems adamant that she won't part with the purée at first, try again in a few days.

Preventing choking

For many children the sloppy first stage of weaning is over in a few weeks. Once they graduate to eating textured foods, the first thing a parent thinks of is the possibility of choking. How can someone so little manage anything that isn't the consistency of soup without it getting stuck? It's nerve wracking for some parents and often means they persist with the purée phase for far too long. Remember it's all about baby steps. Your child has a gag reflex which will prevent her from choking as she learns to deal with different textures. If she gags this doesn't mean she is choking, she is just gagging. This is a protective reflex

and a perfectly normal part of dealing with a lumpier diet. Your child will sound like she's coughing and sputtering momentarily. It tends to be triggered by putting too much food in the mouth or pushing it back too far. It can also be a consequence of a spoon being forced back too far, something that is not uncommon with a novice feeder. In contrast, choking will mean a child makes no noise, is unable to breathe and appears distressed. You don't reduce the choking risk by avoiding the next phase of weaning. Instead, ensure you are always with your child when she is eating, even if she is self-feeding. Sit her upright, fully secured in a high chair, and only ever offer age-appropriate foods.

Top tips for safely swallowing solid foods

Be assured that once your baby is able to easily swallow smooth purées she should be safe to try small lumps in cooked foods.

- Make sure that you have cooked fruits and vegetables enough that there are no hard or raw parts in the purée. If using baby-led weaning, cook vegetables until they can be squashed easily in your fingers.

- Take care when preparing fish or meats like sausages to remove any small bones or pieces of skin. Small round fruits such as grapes or cherry tomatoes should be cut in half.

- Remember to always stay with your child while she is eating and do not leave her to finish off her dinner.

Putting lumps to the test

At this stage you will have established some fruit and veg that baby likes. Instead of pulping it in the processor, mash it with a fork so it's lumpy. Alternatively, mix your regular purée with the mashed version. Baby will then try it, recognize the familiar taste and hopefully tackle the lumps with her gums. No teeth required. A variety of finger foods like toast or fruit slices should also be on offer. Your child will be able to pick these up and put them in her mouth, which will get her used to chewing, as well as improving her co-ordination skills. Ideally these foods should be shaped like batons or cubes to enable your child to grasp as she grazes. Encourage your child to drink from a cup or a beaker. Once she gets over the attraction of free flow she will soon bid goodbye to the bottle. Aim to offer water with every meal. If your child is a milk monster, ensure she doesn't have milk with meals as she will fill herself up and forget about food.

Foods to avoid

Weaning is all about setting your child on the right path to health, not only now but in the future. It is thought that children establish their likes and dislikes by the age of two years, so offering inappropriate or unhealthy foods could have a lasting impact. Children mimic those around them so if you want to establish healthy eating habits, you must lead by example.

Salt

Up until the age of six months your baby's salt requirement is met by either breast milk or commercial formula feeds. Beyond this, the recommendation is 1 gram per day, that's one sixth of the daily requirement for an adult. Babies' kidneys are too immature to deal with adult levels of salt. Bearing in mind most of the salt we eat is 'hidden' in processed and packet foods, these should be off limits for your baby. Highly salted foods such as crisps and bacon should also be off the menu and steer clear of the hidden salt in stock cubes and ready-made sauces. Do not add salt during cooking, e.g. making mash or boiling pasta, if there's any possibility your child is going to be having a baby portion.

Sugar

Avoid sugar wherever possible – giving a sugar rush now will not only lead to a sweet tooth in later life but also increase the risk of tooth decay. Before the age of one year, honey should never be used to sweeten things as it may contain the bacteria *clostridium botulin* which can result in the extremely rare but potentially fatal illness, botulism. Honey can't be added to food, used on a dummy or even put onto ham as a glaze if there is a chance baby is going to eat it. It's off limits.

Nuts

No child should have a whole nut before the age of five years because of the risk of choking and inhalation. Nuts can, however, be given after six months if they are finely ground or used in cooking. Families with a strong history of nut allergy should always seek medical advice.

Dairy

Cows' milk should be avoided until your baby is 12 months old. It is perfectly acceptable to cook with it but it should never form part of a weaning diet in the early stages. All low-fat substances should be avoided. Babies need fat as a source of energy and for certain vitamins. Low-fat options can be started after the second birthday if desired. Unpasteurized and mouldy cheeses should be for adults only.

Fish

While it makes sense to encourage your offspring to eat fish, marlin, swordfish and shark are not suitable as they contain high levels of mercury, which could be potentially damaging to your baby's developing nervous system. Shellfish should also be avoided due to the potential risk of food poisoning.

Allergies

Allergies can run in families so if a parent or sibling has a specific food allergy you must be more vigilant. Aim to feed your little one foods that are least likely to cause an allergic reaction first, then introduce potentially allergy-provoking foods like eggs, fish, wheat, milk, nuts or seeds one at a time. Allow 72 hours in between each allergenic food and don't be tempted to mix – do a single test with a single ingredient so you can establish cause and effect. If your baby developed eczema in the first three months of life, he is more likely to suffer from a food allergy. Remember, he may not react when he first eats a food – it could be on the second or even third or fourth serving. He may come out in a rash, have watery eyes, a runny nose, itchiness and swelling around the face and mouth or diarrhoea and vomiting. Severe symptoms resulting in difficulty breathing and swelling of the tongue and throat are thankfully rare in small children. Allergic reactions may also be delayed.

If your child has lingering symptoms of upset tummy, eczema, reflux or colic, chat to your doctor about the possibility of a food allergy or intolerance.

What foods to avoid at what age

Before 6 months	6–9 months	9–12 months	12–24 months
All dairy foods	All milk apart from breast milk or infant formula.	All milk apart from breast milk or infant formula.	Whole milk can be introduced
Eggs	Undercooked eggs	Undercooked eggs	Undercooked eggs
Wheat and other gluten containing cereals	Gluten can be introduced after six months		
Nuts and seeds	Peanut butter can be introduced after 6 months. Whole nuts should still be avoided	Seeds and finely chopped nuts can be introduced but whole nuts should still be avoided	Whole nuts should be avoided until the age of 5
Unpasteurized cheese	Unpasteurized cheese	Unpasteurized cheese	Unpasteurized cheese
Shellfish	Shellfish	Shellfish	Shellfish
Fish	White fish and oily fish can be introduced		
Meat and poultry	Meat and poultry can be introduced		
Citrus fruits	Citrus fruits	Citrus fruits may be tolerated at this age	
Whole grapes / cherry tomatoes	Whole grapes / cherry tomatoes (chopped is fine)	Whole grapes / cherry tomatoes (chopped is fine)	Whole grapes / cherry tomatoes (chopped is fine)
Salt	Less than 1 g of salt/day	Less than 1 g of salt/day	Less than 2 g of salt/day
Sugar/honey	Sugar/honey	Sugar/honey	Added sugar
Liver	Liver	Liver	

Eating with the family

There is mounting evidence to suggest the benefits of family dining. Throughout my own childhood dinnertime was family time and nothing took precedence over it. Yes, we fought and made a mess, but it provided an excellent forum for everyone to have a catch up, even if some of the party couldn't yet speak. Babies and toddlers love to see the interaction around a dinner table. With our 24/7 lifestyles we often desk-dine at work or eat in the car and children frequently end up eating solo. Your child should never eat unsupervised, no matter how busy you are.

Involving your baby

I can't overemphasize the importance of families sitting together at a table. Ok, your six month old isn't going to tuck into a Sunday roast but she can still enjoy being part of the process. From as early an age as possible, get her involved in the food prep. She doesn't have to actually do anything, she just has to feel like she is taking part. This will help her food curiosity and give her a sense of the immense variety there is when it comes to food. Seeing, touching, feeling and smelling food is just as important as eating it. She is much more likely to taste and experiment with new food concepts if she has 'helped' create the meal. Evidence suggests that those who eat together even three to four nights per week reap the benefits when it comes to health and wellbeing. Children are stimulated and they feel nurtured and there is also the benefit of a predictable daily routine. Even the act of getting them to wash their hands before they prepare food or sit down to eat is a positive outcome. Kids may be chaotic but they fare best when they run like clockwork!

Keep it simple

Try not to overcomplicate things when it comes to child-friendly dining – instead, prepare something that everyone can eat at least part, if not all, of. Avoid spices like chilli, but using small amounts of cumin, coriander or cinnamon is fine. Ready meals and takeaways are fine for grown ups occasionally, but these types of adult meals are inappropriate for babies and toddlers. For those of you on diets, remember children need the full-fat option so blue milk is back in the fridge and low-fat yogurts and so on are out.

Your growing baby

In the first 12 months of life your baby grows the most she ever will. Her weight has probably tripled in this time, something you will testify to when you try to lift her out of the cot! From the age of one to five years her growth slows so you sometimes see a slowing of appetite. As she grows out of the 'baby' phase she will become much more aware and assertive. She will socialize and imitate, so feeding time is a great opportunity to learn new habits. You will find that your child might like to graze rather than eat. She may not fully finish her evening meal and she will get very easily distracted. It's normal, don't get too bogged down with it.

On the move

Sitting round the table with chatter and the clatter of forks and spoons is wonderful, but it's not our everyday reality. We all have to go out to run errands, go to work, take trips or socialize, so there has to be a plan for feeding on the move. As adults, we have a tendency to eat poorly when we are on the hop, a habit we shouldn't pass on to our children. Preparation here is an absolute priority.

The 'going-out' bag

Remember when you were about to give birth and you had a bag at the ready? Your going-out bag should now be on standby, equipped and ready to spring into action at a second's notice. While I was never a great consumer of ready-made baby food, having a stash of these easy meals can be a lifesaver if you're stranded with a hungry child. In terms of snacks, dried fruit and rice cakes can survive for a long time in a bag without going off. Certain brands of straw yogurts can also be kept unrefrigerated for 12 hours. As you dash out the door grab a banana and an apple; both will fill a hunger gap if necessary.

Maintaining routine

Preparing food for a big day out is important as it prevents you from resorting to junk food and it keeps your child in the same eating routine. Prepare all you can the night before. If you are bringing hot food, it can easily be kept warm in a flask while yogurts and other chilled items can be kept in a cooler bag. Children like to have their own things, so invest in a fun lunch box and let your child help you prepare and pack it. Remember, where snacks are concerned, try to opt for less messy foods such as grapes and carrot sticks, and ensure you clean your child's hands before he eats. Wipes are a must! There is always a huge temptation to resort to unhealthy snacks when outside the home but if you can stick to your regular routine, your child won't be expecting a treat at 11am unless you tell him it's on the agenda! That said, I call my daughter's going-out bag my 'fire escape' and keep a stash of chocolate buttons in there for emergencies. Consider it your last resort if the tantrum becomes insurmountable – you may not need to use it, but it's there if things get heated.

Eating out

Eating out might seem like an ordeal but in general it isn't, as long as you choose an appropriate, child-friendly place to eat. A high chair and bib are a must and it's a good idea to bring your own utensils. Your child likes to have things that are familiar to him and it's far easier for you to gauge portion sizes if you have your own plates and bowls. If he is old enough, by all means eat off the children's menu. Stick to your basic principles of having something savoury first, then something sweet. If he won't try something new, suggest he tries a few mouthfuls, but don't force the issue. If you have brought your own food, politely ask the staff to reheat it. Remember, not everyone has children, so test it before your child tastes it to make sure it's cooked to the appropriate temperature.

Leaving your child

If someone else is looking after your child, it's important for them to stick to your feeding routine as closely as possible. The only way you can do this is by giving strict instructions to any nannies, grannies or godparents. They might moan a little about how strict you are with your child's nutrition, but if they want a tantrum-free day they are better off sticking to the established plan. Advise all carers on any allergies or food intolerances and even if they are well versed in child welfare, it's never any harm to remind them what kids can and can't have in a particular age group. Again, come armed with your own utensils, otherwise your little fella might end up eating off a plate the size of his grandmother's head. If you can, bring the high chair too, it all helps.

Lunch box fun

Children like food to be fun. Try to get them involved in preparing food and together give it exciting names. How quickly a carrot can become a dinosaur and hummus develop magic powers! Sandwiches can take on pirate ship shapes and apples can be turned into boats. Children want colour, texture, flavour and fun shapes. Don't overload the lunch box and don't try and trick them by introducing a new food. This is best done at home first. Kids love surprises, so include something exciting to surprise him and he may be more encouraged to eat. Maybe stick a picture of your dog on the back of the lunch box, or pop in a napkin with his favourite TV character on it. Making things fun encourages him to get munching.

Common problems

We all have a relationship with food and it evolves as we evolve. Some children take to solids happily and easily, others are not so keen. Most will go through phases where there is flat-out refusal to eat particular foods, which can be incredibly distressing for parents and carers. I know the embarrassment I felt when my own daughter refused to eat anything green. You begin to question your parenting skills and as a doctor, I questioned my qualifications! But the more I researched the topic, the more I realized that fussy eating is in itself something of a developmental milestone. In fact, about a third of toddlers are fussy eaters, so you're not alone!

Trying new foods

We can be naturally fearful of new things. Where food is concerned, some children exhibit what's known as neophobia – the fear of new foods. It is thought to stem from an evolutionary safety net where we wouldn't try new foods for fear they were poisonous. There seems to be a similar principal behind your baby favouring salty or sweet foods during the weaning process. This is also because she's only ever consumed milk, which is sweet, so it's no surprise that she turns her nose up at vegetable purée. The key is to

always offer savoury before sweet. Let her explore it, play with it and get it all over her face. If at first you don't succeed, try, try... try again! It can sometimes take more than ten attempts to get a child to eat!

Demanding attention

Around about the age of one a child's growth spurt slows down, so she doesn't need to eat as much to meet her energy demands. At the same time she is starting to become more independent, she wants to do things for herself and show you who's boss. Finally your baby realizes that if she causes a riot at feeding time, she will attract more of your much-coveted attention. There is a secondary gain if she creates a mashed potato crisis! She might be small but you can rest assured the internal cogs are turning and she sure knows how to push your buttons. Instead, engage and indulge her with smiles and encouragement! Praise her when she eats well and don't throw a wobbly if she starts spitting, just clear her plate away and move on.

Tips for mealtimes

Structure is essential. Your child is more likely to be fussy if she doesn't have dedicated meal times, so aim for three meals and two snacks each day, with at least two hours between each. Lead by example; children like to model their parents' behaviour, so eat your food with her and be seen to enjoy it! Make food fun by creating different colours, textures and shapes, and give foods fantasy names like Pirate Pasta and Cinderella Sweetcorn. If you expect her to eat, it helps to be creative! When plating up food, less is more. No child wants to be faced with a mountain of mash. It's better to give smaller portions and offer seconds than have her staring at a mound of food. Children are easily distracted, so banish TV and toys from the table

– this goes for mum and dad's smart phones as well. Allocate 20–30 minutes per sitting and then clear the plate away, regardless of how much she's eaten. Try not to be concerned – your baby won't let herself go without food for too long, so stay strong!

What to avoid

Don't fall into the first-time-parent trap like I did and cook multiple meals at dinnertime. The home kitchen should be a one-dish diner, like it or lump it. Try to avoid giving your baby drinks at the start of her meals, because she might fill herself up with milk or water before she's eaten. If there's a particular food she's refused before and it's going for a re-trial, don't remind her that she's previously dismissed it. Finally, avoid trying to introduce foods by stealth – so no hiding vegetables in her pasta hoops, or submerging meat in the mashed potato! If you get busted, she may refuse both foods next time.

Teething

There are a host of medical reasons why your child might refuse food. Teething is a prime suspect, causing pain, drooling and gum swelling. Some children cruise through it, but many show their discomfort at dinnertime. She might become an irritable and fussy dinner guest. In this instance it's time to 'get soft'! Offer food of softer consistency, like stewed apple or egg. Don't force her to eat, as this can ultimately lead to fussy eating in the future. Put cooked carrot sticks in the fridge for her to munch – the cool sensation may ease her discomfort – and avoid serving very hot food or anything with citrus fruit in it, as these will only antagonize the situation.

Planning meals

It's time to use that word which is pivotal in every busy parent's life – planning! Pre-baby, I flew by the seat of my pants and dined in or out, or sometimes not at all. Post-baby, that's gone by the wayside and now my life is planned with military precision. Let's face it, planning saves us time and money and a whole lot of stress! It also means there is a format to your child's dining schedule. Toddlers love routine and ritual, so your little one is much more likely to engage if there is an established food itinerary.

Plan ahead

First of all, make a shopping list. Ensure you have a selection of in-cupboard staples that never go off, such as canned fruit, tuna and sweetcorn. Buy your fruit, veg, fish and meat in season where possible, as it's cheaper and fresher. Remember, you can always prep extra veg and then freeze it for use another day. I'm all in favour of bulk cooking and bunging it in the freezer! Frozen food itself doesn't go off, but it does tend to lose its taste. Remember, freezing doesn't necessarily kill germs, they are just deactivated, so once the food is defrosted you are vulnerable to infection once again. Make sure it doesn't start to heat up once it thaws and in the instance of microwave defrosting, eat the food immediately and bin what you don't eat. Frozen veg can be cooked without defrosting and freezing foods doesn't destroy their nutrient quantity, so your child isn't missing out on anything if you take this shortcut. Even in the event of a power cut most food will remain frozen for 48 hours, but if in doubt, chuck it out. And one final gem – it is possible to freeze milk. This will revolutionize your life if milk is your little one's staple drink!

A healthy routine

Having navigated through purées, when your baby graduates to family food it can be difficult to work out how much of what to give him. I like the 5-5-3-2-a-day regime! He needs four out of the five food groups every day, and only a certain amount of each. Let's start with carbohydrates; he should have five servings of this per day, such as bread, pasta and rice cakes. The next five is fruit and veg, so aim for five servings daily. He needs three servings of dairy produce, such as cheese, yogurt and milk. Finally, he needs two servings of protein, which could be anything from baked beans to minced beef. Try not to include sugary, fatty foods into his regular routine. The occasional treat is totally fine, but don't get into the habit of offering it as a reward for eating his greens! If you are trying a new food you can incorporate it into a favourite meal. In terms of healthy food choices, you decide what's going on the menu, then it's up to him to eat it off the plate. As a parent you have to be the one in control of what, when and where, but the child ultimately decides what goes down the hatch. Routine and structure mean he is much more likely to eat what is necessary.

How much?

Portion sizes are important but often difficult to assess unless the food is on a plate. I tend to work on handfuls (your child's) being a good estimate of size. There are numerous tools online and you can even buy special plates to help work out the amounts of each food group, but after a while you'll get a feel for how your child feeds. Whatever you do, don't compare. We all eat differently as both adults and children but at the end of the day, a healthy baby will eat if he's hungry.

Stage 1
Recipes

The recipes in this section have been selected especially for your baby's first weeks of weaning. With a range of savoury and sweet purées made from vegetables and soft fruits, these recipes are smooth and tasty, helping to bridge the gap between milk and solids.

The suggested meal planner at the end of this chapter can be used for the first week of introducing solid foods. Once your baby has tried a number of individual vegetables and fruits, you can start to introduce blends and offer food at breakfast or dinnertime.

Baby rice

❄ *Makes 8 portions and takes 15 minutes.*

Rice is one of the least allergenic grains and therefore makes a great first-food for babies. To make baby rice, place 40 g / 1 ½ oz / ¼ cup white long-grain rice in a food processor and grind to a powder, then warm 250 ml / 9 fl. oz / 1 cup water in a saucepan until simmering.

Whisk in the ground powder and simmer, whisking constantly, for 5–7 minutes until thickened and creamy. Whisk in 1–2 tbsp of formula or breast milk to achieve the desired consistency. Serve lukewarm or chill until needed.

Baby's first oatmeal

❄ *Makes 8 portions and takes 15 minutes.*

Oatmeal is a tasty and safe option to give your baby early in the weaning process. To make baby's first oatmeal, place 10 g / ¼ oz / ¼ cup rolled oats in a food processor and grind to a fine powder, then warm 250 ml / 9 fl. oz / 1 cup water in a saucepan until simmering.

Whisk in the ground powder and simmer, whisking constantly, for 5–7 minutes until thickened and creamy. Whisk in 1–2 tbsp of formula or breast milk to achieve the desired consistency. Serve lukewarm or chill until needed.

Baby's first barley

❄ *Makes 8 portions and takes 15 minutes.*

Barley makes a nutritious cereal for babies and is a very versatile grain. To make baby's first barley, place 40 g / 1 ½ oz / ¼ cup barley flakes in a food processor and grind to a fine powder, then warm 250 ml / 9 fl. oz / 1 cup water in a saucepan until simmering.

Whisk in the ground powder and simmer, whisking constantly, for 5–7 minutes until thickened and creamy. Whisk in 1–2 tbsp of formula or breast milk to achieve the desired consistency. Serve lukewarm or chill until needed.

Cauliflower purée

Makes 6 portions and takes 20 minutes.

Cauliflower is packed full of vitamins and disease-fighting phytochemicals. To make a purée, simply place 1 small cauliflower, broken into florets, in a metal steaming basket over a small saucepan of boiling water, or cook in enough unsalted boiling water to just cover, for about 8–10 minutes until very soft. Drain, reserving a little of the cooking liquid.

Purée using a stick blender. Add 1–2 tbsp of the cooking water, formula or breast milk and mix to a thin, creamy consistency. Push through a fine sieve into a bowl. Add more cooking water or milk to mix to the desired consistency. Serve lukewarm.

Corn purée

Makes 6 portions and takes 20 minutes.

As a purée, corn is fine to introduce to your baby at this early stage. To make a purée, shave the corn from 2 stalks and place in a metal steaming basket over a small saucepan of boiling water or cook in enough unsalted boiling water to just cover, for about 8–10 minutes until very soft. Drain, reserving a little of the cooking liquid.

Purée using a stick blender. Add 1–2 tbsp of the cooking water, formula or breast milk and mix to a thin, creamy consistency. Push through a fine sieve into a bowl. Add more cooking water or milk to mix to the desired consistency. Serve lukewarm.

Courgette purée

Makes 6 portions and takes 20 minutes.

Courgettes are really easy to make into delicious baby food. Simply place 2 small courgettes (zucchinis), roughly chopped, in a metal steaming basket over a small saucepan of boiling water, or cook in enough unsalted boiling water to just cover, for about 8–10 minutes until very soft. Drain, reserving a little of the cooking liquid.

Purée using a stick blender. Add 1–2 tbsp of the cooking water, formula or breast milk and mix to a thin, creamy consistency. Push through a fine sieve into a bowl. Add more cooking water or milk to mix to the desired consistency. Serve lukewarm.

Pea purée

Makes 6 portions and takes 20 minutes.

Peas are a fantastic first 'green' food for your baby, as they provide a lot of nutritional goodness! Place 150 g / 5 oz / 1 cup frozen peas in a metal steaming basket over a saucepan of boiling water, or cook in enough unsalted boiling water to just cover, for about 8–10 minutes until very soft. Drain, reserving a little of the cooking liquid.

Purée using a stick blender. Add 1–2 tbsp of the cooking water, formula or breast milk and mix to a thin, creamy consistency. Push through a fine sieve into a bowl. Add more cooking water or milk to mix to the desired consistency. Serve lukewarm.

Top tip

Milk will still be your baby's staple food for the first few weeks, as he will probably end up getting very little in terms of calories or nutrition when he initially starts solids. It may seem like it takes forever, but slowly he will get into the swing of things. Anticipate that he might not like his first veggie bite, it's not unusual – and while it is important to be persistent, set yourself a deadline as the worst thing you can do is drag things out. You can always try again in a few days.

Kale and pea purée

❄ *Makes 8 portions and takes 15 minutes.*

Kale is one of the healthiest greens on the market! Considered a 'superfood', kale's nutritional value is high, offering loads of calcium, fibre and protein. It's easy to source and makes a very tasty purée.

Cook 150 g / 5 oz / 1 cup frozen peas with 140 g / 5 oz / 2 cups chopped curly kale in a large saucepan of boiling water for 8–10 minutes. Drain and refresh in iced water. Purée with ½ tbsp butter in a food processor until smooth. Thin with boiled water, formula or breast milk. Serve lukewarm or cold. The garnish is optional and not suitable for babies.

Carrot purée

❄ *Makes 8 portions and takes 20 minutes.*

Carrots are one of the best first foods for babies: they're packed full of beta-carotene, vitamins and calcium, they're easy to digest, and they have a gentle flavour.

To make a carrot purée, peel and dice 4 large carrots. Boil the carrots in a large saucepan of water for 14–16 minutes until tender. Drain and transfer to a food processor, then add 1 tbsp butter and pulse until you have a thick purée. Thin with boiled water, formula or breast milk. Serve cold or lukewarm. The garnish is optional and not suitable for babies.

Broccoli purée

❄ *Makes 8 portions and takes 10 minutes.*

A simple broccoli purée is an easy way to offer baby all the nutritional goodness of this mighty green vegetable.

Cut 1 large head of broccoli into florets, then cook in a large saucepan of boiling water for 3–4 minutes until tender. Drain and reserve the cooking liquor. Purée the florets with a little of the cooking liquid until smooth. Serve lukewarm or cold. The garnish is optional and not suitable for babies.

Squash purée

❄ *Makes 8 portions and takes 25 minutes.*

When puréed, butternut squash has a delicious, smooth texture, making it ideal for one of baby's first foods. It contains vitamins and calcium which contribute to your baby's dietary requirements, and has a unique and delicious flavour.

To make a squash purée, peel, seed and cube 1 small butternut squash. Cook the squash in a large saucepan of boiling water for 15–20 minutes until soft. Drain and purée in a food processor, then add ½ tbsp butter and 1 tsp tomato purée and blitz again until smooth. Thin as desired with breast or formula milk or boiled water. Serve lukewarm or cold. The garnish is optional and not suitable for babies.

Banana purée

Makes 8 portions and takes 10 minutes.

Bananas are nutritious, mushy and delicious – perfect for baby's first foods! Rich in potassium and fibre, they're an essential component of a healthy diet.

Purée 2 small, ripe bananas in a food processor until smooth. Add 1–2 tbsp formula or breast milk and mix to the desired consistency. Serve immediately or cover and chill until needed.

Papaya purée

Makes 8 portions and takes 10 minutes.

Babies love sweet foods, so papaya will go down a treat in this delicious and simple purée. They're also packed with vitamins, so you can be sure these tropical fruits are doing a whole lot of good!

Peel, seed and dice 1 ripe papaya. Purée the papaya with 2–3 tbsp water in a food processor. Thin the purée with more water if needed. Cover and chill until needed or serve at room temperature.

Apple purée

Makes 8 portions and takes 15 minutes.

Apples are ideal first foods – they keep the digestive system in order and provide the right nutrients for a healthy diet.

To make a purée, peel, core and dice 2 Gala apples. Combine the apple with 4–5 tbsp pure apple juice or water in a saucepan, then cook over a medium heat for 6–8 minutes until very soft. Purée in a food processor and thin with a little more water or apple juice if needed. Cover and chill until needed or serve lukewarm.

Pear purée

Makes 8 portions and takes 15 minutes.

Pears are very gentle fruits for your baby's tummy, and are high in potassium, fibre and essential vitamins.

To make a purée, peel, core and dice 2 Rocha pears. Combine the pear and 4 tbsp water in a saucepan. Cook over a medium heat for 5–6 minutes until very soft. Purée in a food processor and thin with a little more water if needed. Allow to cool before serving or cover and chill until needed.

Peach purée

Makes 8 portions and takes 10 minutes.

As well as being deliciously sweet and juicy, peaches are very soft, making them a great first food for your baby. They contain plenty of vitamins and fibre to keep the digestive system in order.

Cut a shallow cross in the skin of 2 peaches, then place them in a small saucepan of boiling water until tender. Plunge into cold water to refresh, then skin and chop the peaches, discarding the stones. Purée with a stick blender, then cover and chill until needed.

Plum purée

Makes 8 portions and takes 10 minutes.

Plums are incredibly nutritious fruits, offering plenty of fibre, vitamin A and C, and are low in cholesterol and sodium. As such, they're great for digestion.

Cut a shallow cross in the skin of 6 plums and place in a small saucepan of boiling water until tender. Plunge into cold water to refresh, then skin and chop the plums, discarding the stones, and purée with a stick blender. Cover and chill until needed.

Blueberry purée

Makes 9 portions and takes 10 minutes.

Blueberries are considered a 'super food', which makes them one of nature's most nutritious and healthy foods. Packed with antioxidants, fibre and vitamins, they're a wonderful first food for babies and make a fun, purple-blue purée!

Combine 150 g / 5 oz / 1 cup washed blueberries and 2 tbsp pure apple juice in a saucepan. Cook over a low heat until the blueberries are soft and juicy. Blend with a stick blender. Pass the mixture through a fine sieve into a bowl and cover and chill until needed or serve lukewarm.

Raspberry purée

Makes 9 portions and takes 10 minutes.

Raspberry purée is a wonderfully sweet treat for babies and its bright colour will grab their attention. Try to source fresh raspberries when in season, as these will be a better quality and taste for baby's new palate.

Combine 140 g / 5 oz / 1 cup washed raspberries and 1 tbsp hot water in a food processor. Purée until smooth, then pass through a fine sieve into a bowl. Cover and chill until needed or serve lukewarm.

Mango purée

Makes 9 portions and takes 10 minutes.

Tropical fruits like mango are easy to purée because they're soft and fleshy, and their sweet, exotic flavour will really appeal to your baby. Save larger mango pieces for when she's ready for finger foods, and stick to mushy mango for now!

Pit, peel and dice 1 ripe mango, then combine it with 1 tbsp water in a food processor. Purée until smooth. Cover and chill until needed or serve lukewarm.

Prune purée

Makes 9 portions and takes 15 minutes.

Prunes are a good first food. They're great for supporting the digestive system and will be gentle on baby's tummy. Try them by themselves or combine with baby rice.

Soak 150 g / 5 oz / 1 cup washed prunes in 4 tbsp hot water in a bowl for 10 minutes. Transfer the prunes and water to a food processor and purée until smooth. Cover and chill until needed or serve lukewarm.

Top tip

These fruit purées will go down a treat, but don't forget the importance of introducing plenty of savoury foods, too.

Fresh fruits are best when in season, but many purées can be made with thawed frozen fruits. Remember, too, that you can make a batch of purée and freeze in small portions for later. A big part of parenting is being organized, so don't be afraid to cut corners in the kitchen. It will save you time and energy in the long run!

Banana and avocado purée

Makes 8 portions and takes 10 minutes.

1 large, ripe banana, peeled and diced

1 small, ripe avocado, pitted and diced

- Purée the banana and avocado in a food processor with 1–2 tbsp formula or breast milk. Serve soon after making.

Apple and squash purée

Makes 8 portions and takes 15 minutes.

1 Gala apple, peeled, cored and diced

1 small butternut squash, peeled, seeded and diced

- Combine the apple and squash in a steaming basket over a small saucepan of boiling water and steam for 10 minutes until very soft.
- Purée the cooked apple and squash with 1–2 tbsp water, formula or breast milk until smooth. Cover and chill until needed or serve lukewarm.

Beetroot and apple purée

Makes 8 portions and takes 10 minutes.

150 g / 5 oz / 1 cup cooked beetroot in juice, drained and diced

1 Gala apple, peeled, cored and diced

1 tbsp water

- Combine the beetroot and apple in a saucepan with the water. Cook over a medium heat for 5–6 minutes until the apple is soft.
- Purée in a food processor until smooth. Cover and chill until needed or serve lukewarm.

Parsnip and pea purée

Makes 8 portions and takes 15 minutes.

2 small parsnips, peeled and sliced

150 g / 5 oz / 1 cup frozen peas

½ tbsp butter

- Cook the parsnip and peas in a large saucepan of unsalted boiling water for about 10 minutes until very soft. Drain well, reserving a little cooking liquid.
- Purée the parsnips and peas with a little cooking liquid in a food processor. Cover and chill until needed or serve lukewarm.

Banana and apple purée

Makes 8 portions and takes 15 minutes.

1 Gala apple, peeled, cored and diced

2 tbsp water

1 large, ripe banana, peeled and diced

- Combine the apple and water in a saucepan. Cook over a medium heat for 5 minutes until softened. Combine with the banana in a food processor and purée until smooth. Thin down with water, formula or breast milk if desired. Cover and chill until needed or serve lukewarm.

Blueberry, apple and peach purée

Makes 8 portions and takes 15 minutes.

75 g / 2 ½ oz / ½ cup blueberries, washed

1 Gala apple, peeled, cored and diced

1 ripe peach, pitted and diced

2 tbsp water

- Combine the blueberry, apple, peach and water in saucepan. Cook over a medium heat for 5–6 minutes until the apple is tender. Transfer the fruit and juices to a food processor and blend until smooth. Cover and chill until needed or serve lukewarm.

Carrot and orange purée

Makes 8 portions and takes 25–30 minutes.

2 large carrots, peeled and diced

2 tbsp pure orange juice

- Place the carrots in a steaming basket set atop a half-filled saucepan of boiling water. Steam for 15–20 minutes until very tender.
- Combine the cooked carrot with the orange juice in a food processor. Purée until smooth. Cover and chill until needed or serve lukewarm.

Potato and leek purée

Makes 8 portions and takes 25–30 minutes.

2 floury potatoes, peeled and diced

½ small leek, sliced and washed

½ tbsp butter

- Place the potato and leek separately in a steaming basket set atop a half-filled saucepan of boiling water. Steam for 18–22 minutes until very tender.
- Mash the potato with the butter until very smooth. Purée the leek in a food processor with 1–2 tbsp of the cooking water, formula or breast milk and blend until smooth.
- Mix together the potato and leek purée and thin as desired with formula or breast milk. Cover and chill until needed or serve lukewarm.

Stage 1 meal planner

	Monday	Tuesday	Wednesday
Wake Up	Milk	Milk	Milk
Mid Morning	Milk	Milk	Milk
Lunch	Milk – baby rice	Milk – carrot purée	Milk – squash purée
Mid Afternoon	Milk	Milk	Milk
Evening	Milk	Milk	Milk

Thursday	Friday	Saturday	Sunday
Milk	Milk	Milk	Milk
Milk	Milk	Milk	Milk
Milk – banana purée	Milk – broccoli purée	Milk – cauliflower purée	Milk – mango purée
Milk	Milk	Milk	Milk
Milk	Milk	Milk	Milk

Stage 2
Recipes

Once your baby has reached stage 2 (usually 7–9 months) she should have increased her food intake to 2–3 meals a day. The recipes in this section are more textured and chunky, including options that are suitable for breakfast, lunch and dinner. The fruity recipes also work as a dessert if you feel that your baby isn't content after her savoury meal.

The meal planner at the end of this section is based on your baby eating three meals a day and has been designed to provide a balance of food groups each day and to offer an iron rich meal once a week. The milk feed that has been suggested for the afternoon can be changed for the morning if this works better for your baby.

Sweet potato and red pepper purée

❄ *Makes 8 portions and takes 20 minutes.*

Sweet potatoes are loaded with vitamin A, beta carotene and potassium, making this a super-healthy choice for baby. Alongside peppers, which also contain folates and vitamins A, B6 and C, this purée is sweet enough for baby's new palate and is a great way to introduce healthy vegetables into his diet.

1 medium sweet potato,
    peeled and diced

1 red pepper, seeded and diced

½ tbsp butter

- Place the sweet potato and pepper in a metal steaming basket over a small saucepan of boiling water, or cook in enough unsalted boiling water to cover, for about 10 minutes until very soft.
- Drain, reserving the cooking liquid, then purée using a stick blender. Add 1–2 tbsp of the cooking water and the butter, then mix to a purée while retaining a little texture. Serve lukewarm.

Courgette and potato purée

❄ *Makes 8 portions and takes 30 minutes.*

This purée combines carbohydrates from the potato with all the green goodness of the courgette, providing plenty of vitamins for your baby's diet. The courgette gives this mashed-potato mix a wonderful colour and flavour that will appeal to baby's new tastes.

2 large floury potatoes,
    peeled and diced

1 courgette (zucchini), diced

½ tbsp butter

- Place the potato and courgette separately in a steaming basket over a small saucepan of boiling water for about 12–14 minutes until soft.
- Drain, reserving the cooking liquid, then mash the potatoes. Purée the courgette with a stick blender, adding 1–2 tbsp of the cooking water and the butter. Mix together the potato and courgette purée and thin as desired with formula or breast milk. Serve lukewarm.

Cauliflower cheese

❄ *Makes 8 portions and takes 30 minutes.*

This is the perfect time to introduce cauliflower into your baby's diet. Packed with helpful phtyochemicals, vitamins A and C and calcium, it's a great addition to a healthy diet. This creamy, cheesy mix will soon become one of baby's favourites!

1 head cauliflower, broken into florets

1 medium floury potato,
    peeled and diced

1 tbsp Cheddar cheese, grated

- Place the cauliflower and potato separately in a metal steaming basket over a small saucepan of boiling water, or cook in enough unsalted boiling water to cover, for about 12–14 minutes until very soft.
- Drain, reserving the cooking liquid, then mash the potato. Purée the cauliflower using a stick blender, adding 1–2 tbsp of the cooking water and the cheese. Mix together the potato and cauliflower purées and thin as desired using formula or breast milk. Serve lukewarm.

Squash and cannellini bean purée

❄ Makes 8 portions and takes 15 minutes.

Butternut squash makes a beautiful, smooth purée that's packed with vitamins and calcium, so it's an ideal candidate for baby's first foods. You can mash these hearty vegetables to whatever thickness your baby is ready for, and they can be left a bit more chunky when he's experimenting with finger food.

1 small butternut squash, peeled, seeded and diced

200 g / 7 oz / 1 cup canned cannellini beans, drained and rinsed

- Cook the squash in a large saucepan of unsalted boiling water for 10 minutes. Add the beans and continue to cook for a further 4–5 minutes until tender.
- Drain well, reserving some of the cooking liquid and mash with a couple of tablespoons of this liquid until the texture of mashed potato. Cover and chill or serve lukewarm.

Avocado and pea purée

❄ Makes 8 portions and takes 10 minutes.

Avocados are another one of nature's 'superfoods' – they're packed with good fats that will help baby's physical and brain development, and are an all-round nutritious boost of green goodness! The creamy texture of this purée makes it a perfect food in the weaning process.

150 g / 5 oz / 1 cup frozen peas

1 medium, ripe avocado, pitted and diced

½ tbsp olive oil

- Cook the peas in a large saucepan of unsalted boiling water for 4–5 minutes until very tender.
- Drain well, reserving some of the cooking liquid, and mash in a bowl with the avocado, olive oil and a couple of tablespoons of the cooking water. Cover and chill or serve lukewarm.

Beetroot and sweet potato purée

❄ Makes 8 portions and takes 20 minutes.

Beetroot and sweet potatoes are a collective powerhouse of potassium, fibre, calcium and vitamins, making this purée a perfect early food for growing babies! When mashed together they create a wonderful, bright colour that will engage your baby during mealtimes, encouraging him to get stuck in.

1 medium sweet potato, peeled and diced

150 g / 5 oz / 1 cup cooked beetroot in juice, drained and chopped

½ tbsp butter

- Cook the sweet potato in a large saucepan of unsalted boiling water for 12–14 minutes until tender.
- Drain well and mash with the butter until the texture of mashed potato. Mash or purée the beetroot and mix with the sweet potato. Cover and chill or serve lukewarm.

Carrot and tomato stew

❄ *Makes 8 portions and takes 25 minutes.*

Carrots are excellent first foods for babies, so they may already play a part in your baby's diet. Now is the perfect time to introduce tomatoes, which provide vitamin C to help with iron absorption. This is a wonderful, bright mash to get her taste buds tingling.

2 large carrots, peeled and diced

**2 vine tomatoes, cored,
  seeded and diced**

½ tbsp olive oil

- Cook the carrots in a large saucepan of unsalted boiling water for 8–10 minutes until tender.
- Drain well, reserving a little cooking water, and combine with the tomato, olive oil and a couple of tablespoons of the cooking liquid in a saucepan. Cover and cook over a low heat for 10–12 minutes, stirring occasionally.
- Mash roughly and leave to cool. Serve lukewarm or chill until needed.

Red pepper and goats' cheese

❄ *Makes 8 portions and takes 35–40 minutes.*

Adding goats' cheese to roasted peppers is a great way to infuse some of the 'good fats' and protein into your baby's diet, as well as introducing new flavours and textures. Now that baby is old enough to try new foods, experiment with other appropriate cheeses such cottage cheese.

2 red peppers

1 vine tomato, cored, seeded and diced

2 tbsp soft goats' cheese

- Preheat the grill to hot. Grill the peppers, turning occasionally, until blistered and blackened all over. Place the peppers in a bag and tie well to seal. Leave to cool for 15 minutes.
- Peel the skin from the peppers and discard any seeds and ribs. Roughly chop the flesh and combine with the tomato and 1 tbsp of water in a small saucepan. Cover and cook over a low heat for 8–10 minutes, stirring occasionally.
- Stir through the goats' cheese and roughly mash. Leave to cool slightly. Serve lukewarm or chill until needed.

Peach and pear purée

Makes 8 portions and takes 10 minutes.

1 ripe peach, pitted and diced

1 ripe Rocha pear, peeled, cored
and diced

2 tbsp pure apple juice

- Combine the peach and pear in a food processor with the apple juice.
- Pulse a few times until a chunky purée comes together, then chill until needed.

Apple and plum purée

Makes 8 portions and takes 10 minutes.

1 Gala apple, peeled, cored and diced

2 plums, pitted and diced

2 tbsp pure apple juice

- Combine the apple, plum and apple juice in a saucepan. Cook over a medium heat for 5–6 minutes until softened.
- Mash into a chunky purée. If necessary, any tough plum skins can be removed by sieving the purée. Cover and chill until needed.

Berry–cherry purée

Makes 8 portions and takes 10 minutes.

150 g / 5 oz / 1 cup cherries,
pitted and chopped

100 g / 3 ½ oz / ⅔ cup blueberries,
washed

2 tbsp water

- Combine the cherries, blueberries and water in a food processor.
- Pulse a few times until a chunky purée comes together, then serve or chill until needed.

Top tip

One of the main questions parents ask when it comes to mushing up baby foods is whether to use a food processor or a blender. Essentially, both are fine for purée-making.

Food processors tend to hold more and are better equipped for puréeing a wider variety of solid foods, although that doesn't mean that your blender won't do the trick. Typically, blenders are ideal for mixing liquids, or mushy solids, whereas food processors perform more functions, giving you more control over how you process your ingredients.

Apple and banana barley

❄ *Makes 8 portions and takes 10 minutes.*

Barley is a highly nutritious grain that's easy for babies to digest, plus it's versatile so will become a staple ingredient in your baby-food cupboard. Apple and banana add an extra burst of nutrition and flavour, encouraging your baby to explore thicker textures and combined flavours.

2 tbsp barley flakes

½ Gala apple, peeled, cored and diced

½ small, ripe banana, chopped

110 ml / 4 fl. oz / ½ cup hot water

- Grind the barley in a food processor until finely ground. Add the apple, banana and hot water to the processor and purée.
- Scrape into a saucepan and cook over a low heat, stirring frequently, for 3–4 minutes. Add more water if necessary, and stir in a little formula or breast milk for a creamier consistency. Serve lukewarm or chill until needed.

Plum and oatmeal purée

❄ *Makes 8 portions and takes 10 minutes.*

Adding fruit to oaty cereals gives an extra depth of flavour, introducing your baby to new foods and textures. Plums are really easy to purée because they're soft, plus they're gentle on baby's tummy. Fresh plums are best for baby food.

20 g / ¾ oz / ½ cup rolled oats

1 plum, pitted and chopped

110 ml / 4 fl. oz / ½ cup hot water

- Grind the oats in a food processor until finely ground. Add the plum and hot water to the processor and purée.
- Scrape into a saucepan and cook over a low heat, stirring frequently, for 3–4 minutes. Add more water if necessary, and stir in a little formula or breast milk for a creamier consistency. Serve lukewarm or chill until needed.

Banana and oatmeal purée

❄ *Makes 8 portions and takes 10 minutes.*

Banana and oats make a great combination at breakfast. When baby is able to chew food, leave bigger chunks of banana in this purée to help her develop those all-important oral motor skills.

20 g / ¾ oz / ½ cup rolled oats

1 small, ripe banana, chopped

110 ml / 4 fl. oz / ½ cup hot water

- Grind the oats in a food processor until finely ground. Add the banana and hot water to the processor and purée.
- Scrape into a saucepan and cook over a low heat, stirring frequently, for 3–4 minutes. Add more water if necessary, and stir in a little formula or breast milk for a creamier consistency. Serve lukewarm or chill until needed.

Apricot and millet purée

Makes 8 portions and takes 15 minutes.

50 g / 1 ¾ oz / ¼ cup millet

150 ml / 5 fl. oz / ⅔ cup hot water

2 apricots, pitted and diced

- Combine the millet, water and apricot in a food processor and leave to soak for 5 minutes until softened. Pulse a few times to combine, then scrape into a saucepan. Cook over a low heat, stirring frequently, for 3–4 minutes until soft, adding more water if necessary.
- Stir in a little formula or breast milk for a creamier consistency. Serve lukewarm or chill until needed.

Tropical fruit porridge

Makes 8 portions and takes 15 minutes.

20 g / ¾ oz / ½ cup rolled oats

110 ml / 4 fl. oz / ½ cup hot water

½ mango, pitted and diced

2 tbsp pineapple chunks in juice, drained

- Combine the oats, water, mango and pineapple in a food processor and leave to soak for 5 minutes until softened. Pulse a few times to combine, then scrape into a saucepan. Cook over a low heat, stirring frequently, for 3–4 minutes until soft, adding more water if necessary.
- Stir in a little formula or breast milk for a creamier consistency. Serve lukewarm or chill until needed.

Top tip

Grains are incredibly versatile and can be introduced into the weaning diet early to bridge the gap between milk and solids. They also have great nutritional value.

Millet is rich in B vitamins, potassium and iron, and is ideal as a base for cereals, adding texture and thickness to baby's dishes. She may even try to spoon it in with her fingers when she's ready for finger foods. Oatmeal is also a great starter-solid, high in fibre, calcium and protein.

Beef and sweet potato

Makes 8 portions and takes 1 hour.

Beef is high in protein and iron, which is important in your baby's diet at this stage in his development. It's easily digestible for little ones, so is a great first meat for him to try.

1 tbsp butter

150 g / 5 oz / 1 cup braising steak, cubed

150 g / 5 oz / 1 cup sweet potato, peeled and chopped

250 ml / 9 fl. oz / 1 cup low-sodium chicken stock

75 ml / 2 ½ fl. oz / ⅓ cup orange juice

- Melt the butter in casserole dish, then sauté the steak and sweet potato for about 5 minutes until softened and browned.
- Add the stock and orange juice. Cook until boiling, then cover and reduce to a gentle simmer for 40–45 minutes until the beef is tender.
- Blend to the desired consistency in a food processor using some of the cooking liquid as necessary. Serve lukewarm or chill until needed.

Lamb and apricot

Makes 8 portions and takes 40 minutes.

This is a really simple meat dish that will introduce your baby to the slightly richer flavour of lamb. Apricots are a great accompaniment because they contain a powerful set of disease-fighting nutrients and will bring a lovely level of sweetness to this dish.

1 tbsp butter

150 g / 5 oz / 1 cup lamb shoulder, cubed

2 apricots, pitted and diced

200 ml / 7 fl. oz / ¾ cup low-sodium lamb stock

- Combine the butter, lamb, apricots, stock and enough water to cover in a saucepan. Cook over a moderate heat until boiling, then reduce to a gentle simmer for 30 minutes until the lamb is tender.
- Blend to the desired consistency in a food processor using some of the cooking liquid as necessary. Serve lukewarm or chill until needed.

Chicken and kohlrabi

Makes 8 portions and takes 30 minutes.

If you've never come across kohlrabi before, it's not as exotic as it sounds! A vegetable in the cabbage family, it has a mild, sweet flavour and is usually green, although there is a rarer purple variety, too.

150 g / 5 oz / 1 cup chicken breast, diced

1 small, floury potato, peeled and diced

½ kohlrabi, leaves removed, peeled and diced

½ tbsp butter

- Place the chicken, potato and kohlrabi in a saucepan and add enough water to just cover.
- Cook over a medium-low heat for 15–20 minutes until the chicken is cooked through. Drain well, reserving a couple of tablespoons of cooking liquid, then combine with the butter and cooking liquid in a food processor. Purée until you have the desired consistency. Serve lukewarm or chill until needed.

Turkey, rice, carrot and broccoli

Makes 8 portions and takes 30 minutes.

Turkey is an easily-digestible meat that provides plenty of iron for baby's nutritional requirements. This recipe combines the protein-packed meat with familiar vegetables in a straightforward one-pot dish.

150 g / 5 oz / 1 cup turkey breast, diced

½ head broccoli, broken into florets

1 medium, floury potato, peeled and diced

75 g / 2 ½ oz / ½ cup cooked white rice

1 large carrot, peeled and grated

- Combine the turkey, broccoli and potato in a saucepan and add enough water to just cover.
- Cook over a moderate heat until boiling, then reduce to a gentle simmer for 15–20 minutes. Add the cooked rice and carrot and mash well with a potato masher. Serve lukewarm or chill until needed.

Chicken and veg curry

Makes 8 portions and takes 25 minutes.

A mild curry is a great way to introduce your baby to spices. The best thing about this dish is that it can feed the whole family – simply mash baby's portion so she can enjoy the same food as everyone else.

150 g / 5 oz / 1 cup chicken breast, diced

1 medium, floury potato, peeled and diced

1 tsp mild curry paste

½ tbsp butter

55 g / 2 oz / 1 cup baby spinach

- Combine the chicken, potato, curry paste and butter in a saucepan. Add enough water to cover and cook over a moderate heat until boiling.
- Reduce to a gentle simmer and cook for 15 minutes until the potato is tender. Add the baby spinach and cook until wilted, then mash with a potato masher. Serve lukewarm or chill until needed.

Salmon and broccoli pasta

Makes 8 portions and takes 25 minutes.

Fish is important for your baby's brain development, nervous system and vision, and this salmon dish is a great way to get omega 3 into her diet. It also has a good helping of protein.

85 g / 3 oz / ½ cup orzo pasta

½ tbsp olive oil

150 g / 5 oz / 1 cup skinless salmon fillet, pin-boned and diced

1 small head broccoli, broken into florets

- Combine the orzo and olive oil in a saucepan and add enough water to cover. Cook over a moderate heat until boiling, then reduce to a simmer and cook for 7–8 minutes until tender. Drain and put to one side.
- Add the salmon and broccoli to the pan, then add enough water to cover. Cook over a moderate heat until boiling, then reduce to a simmer for 8–10 minutes until the broccoli is tender.
- Remove from the heat, drain and mash well. Add the orzo, then mash again briefly to incorporate. Serve lukewarm or chill until needed.

Chicken and cottage cheese

Makes 8 portions and takes 30 minutes.

Cottage cheese is an ideal cheese to introduce to your baby early on. It's rich in calcium, 'good fats' and protein, and its lumpy texture is ideal for this stage of weaning. Cottage cheese adds subtle flavours to the chicken in this dish, and it'll soon become a firm favourite.

150 g / 5 oz / 1 cup chicken breast, diced

1 small, floury potato, peeled and diced

55 g / 2 oz / ¼ cup cottage cheese

- Place the chicken and potato in a saucepan and add enough water to just cover. Cook over a medium-low heat for 15–20 minutes until the chicken is cooked through.
- Drain well, reserving a couple of tablespoons of cooking liquid, then combine with the cottage cheese and cooking liquid in a food processor. Purée until you have the desired consistency. Serve lukewarm or chill until needed.

White fish and potato mash

Makes 8 portions and takes 25 minutes.

This little version of fish pie is a must-try for babies! Mashed potato is sure to be a favourite already, and introducing cod in this creamy concoction is a great way to give him the essential nutrients that fish provides.

150 g / 5 oz / 1 cup skinless cod fillet

2 small, floury potatoes, peeled, diced

½ tbsp butter

3 tbsp semi-skimmed milk

1 tbsp flat-leaf parsley, chopped

- Pin-bone and dice the cod. Combine the cod, potato, butter and milk in a saucepan and add enough water to cover.
- Cook over a moderate heat until boiling, then reduce to a gentle simmer for 15 minutes until the potato is tender. Add the parsley and mash well with a potato masher. Serve lukewarm or chill until needed.

Lamb with lentils

Makes 8 portions and takes 40 minutes.

Lentils are powerful little things! They're a good source of protein, fibre, vitamin C and beta-carotene, and make a nutritious purée on their own. Combined here with lamb and potato, this simple dish is a delicious provider of protein for your little one.

150 g / 5 oz / 1 cup lamb shoulder, trimmed and diced

85 g / 3 oz / ½ cup green lentils

1 small, floury potato, peeled and diced

½ tbsp butter

- Combine the lamb, lentils, potato and butter in a saucepan and add enough water to cover. Cook over a moderate heat until boiling, then reduce to a gentle simmer for 30 minutes or until the lamb and lentils are very tender.
- Process the mixture in a food processor until puréed. Serve lukewarm or chill until needed.

Stage 2 meal planner

	Monday	Tuesday	Wednesday
Wake Up	Milk	Milk	Milk
Breakfast	Plum and oatmeal	Peach and pear	Berry-cherry
Lunch	Milk – squash and cannellini bean	Milk – chicken and veg curry	Milk – salmon and broccoli pasta
Mid Afternoon	Milk	Milk	Milk
Dinner	Avocado and pea	Beetroot and sweet potato	Cauliflower cheese
Evening	Milk	Milk	Milk

Thursday	Friday	Saturday	Sunday
Milk	Milk	Milk	Milk
Apple and banana barley	Tropical fruit porridge	Apricot and millet	Apple and plum
Milk – lamb and apricot	Milk – turkey, rice, carrot and broccoli	Milk – white fish and potato mash	Milk – chicken and cottage cheese
Milk	Milk	Milk	Milk
Sweet potato and red pepper	Carrot and tomato stew	Red pepper and goats' cheese	Courgette and potato
Milk	Milk	Milk	Milk

Stage 3
Recipes

By now your little one should be enjoying three meals a day and regularly eating foods from each of the food groups. Your baby will still require milk feeds of 500–600 ml a day, but may be snacking more, too! Many of these recipes are suitable for the whole family, so you can optimize your time in the kitchen, waste less and plan your weekly meals more easily.

This chapter gives ideas for breakfast, lunch and dinner, as well as offering suggestions for finger foods. The meal planner at the end suggests a milk feed in the afternoon, but she may not need this now that she's eating more at mealtimes. When your baby drops this feed, be aware that she will require an extra portion of dairy in her diet.

Granola with raspberries

Makes 8 portions and takes 40 minutes.

Now that your baby is well on the way to eating solids, her new teeth will be put to good use on this crunchy, fruity granola. Make plenty in advance and store in an airtight container for up to a week.

40 g / 1 ½ oz / 1 cup rolled oats

1 tbsp honey

1 tbsp sunflower oil

a few drops of vanilla extract

100 g / 3 ½ oz / ⅔ cup raspberries,
   to serve

- Preheat the oven to 170°C (150°C fan) / 325F / gas 3.
- Combine the oats, honey, sunflower oil, vanilla extract and 1 tbsp of water in a mixing bowl. Mix with a spoon to combine. Spread out on a small baking tray and bake for 22–25 minutes until golden.
- Leave to cool and harden before storing. Serve with raspberries.

   NOTE: Not suitable for babies under 12 months.

Fruity muesli

Makes 8 portions and takes 15 minutes plus chilling time.

The beauty of this stage of weaning is that you no longer need to pulse all meals into a mush for your baby! Larger chunks of fruit combined with soft oats will be an easy task for her, now that she's developing those all-important chomping skills.

4 tbsp rolled oats

75 ml / 2 ½ fl. oz / ⅓ cup
   semi-skimmed milk

1 Gala apple, peeled, cored and
   chopped

1 small, ripe pear, peeled, cored and
   chopped

2 tbsp pure apple juice

- Combine the oats and milk in a bowl. Cover and chill for at least 2 hours.
- Combine the apple and pear with the apple juice in a small saucepan. Cook over a medium-low heat for 8–10 minutes until soft. Mash briefly and stir into the soaked oats.
- Serve lukewarm or chill until needed.

Simple scrambled egg

Makes 4 portions and takes 10 minutes.

Scrambled egg should be a staple recipe in your repertoire. It's easy, filling and great for introducing babies to firmer foods. Serve with strips of buttered toast or some baked beans for baby, and allow the rest of the family to dig in, too.

4 large eggs

2 tbsp whole milk

1 tbsp butter

a little pepper

- Thoroughly beat together the eggs, milk and a little pepper in a mixing bowl.
- Heat the butter in a large saucepan set over a medium heat until hot. Add the beaten egg and cook until softly set and scrambled, stirring with a wooden spoon frequently.
- Leave to cool before serving.

Mini fruit rolls

Makes 8 portions and takes 2 hours 30 minutes.

If you have time, home-made bread is totally worth the effort. This fruit bread is an absolute treat for the whole family and your baby will love those sweet, fruity bursts. Top with jams or the occasional chocolate spread for an extra treat.

400 g / 14 oz / 2 ⅔ cups strong white bread flour, plus extra for dusting

½ tsp easy-blend dried yeast

1 tbsp caster (superfine) sugar

1 tsp fine sea salt

100 g / 4 oz / ½ cup mixed dried fruit

1 tbsp butter, melted

1 egg, beaten

- Mix together the flour, yeast, sugar, salt and dried fruit. Stir the butter into 280 ml / 9 fl. oz / 1 cup of warm water. Stir the liquid into the dry ingredients, then knead on a lightly oiled surface for 10 minutes or until the dough is smooth and elastic.
- Leave the dough to rest, covered with oiled cling film, for 1–2 hours or until doubled in size.
- Knead the dough for 2 more minutes, then split it into eight even pieces and create an animal shape from each of these. Transfer the rolls to a greased baking tray and cover with oiled cling film. Leave to prove for 1 hour or until doubled in size.
- Meanwhile, preheat the oven to 220°C (200°C fan) / 425F / gas 7.
- When the dough has risen, brush the tops of the rolls with beaten egg, then transfer the tray to the top shelf of the oven and close the door. Bake for 15 minutes or until the rolls sound hollow when you tap them underneath. Transfer to a wire rack and leave to cool completely.

Mini rice cakes

Makes 8 portions and takes 3 hours.

Mini versions of foods are ideal for weaning babies because they make fantastic finger foods. Babies at stage 3 will be keen to start picking things up, exploring them and mimicking what the rest of the family are doing. These rice cakes will disappear quickly when baby gets her hands on them!

250 g / 9 oz / 1 ½ cups long-grain rice, rinsed

2 tbsp sunflower oil

cream cheese, to serve

peanut butter, to serve

- Cook the rice according to the packet instructions. Once cooked, remove from the heat and leave to cool, covered, for 10 minutes. Fluff the rice with a fork and spread out in a thin layer on a large baking tray.
- Preheat the oven to 130°C (110°C fan) / 275F / gas ½. Grease a large, rimmed baking tray with the sunflower oil.
- Once the rice has cooled down, pack it into the rimmed baking tray, approximately 2.5 cm (1 in) thick. Bake for 1 ½–2 hours until dry and starting to colour on top. Remove from the oven and leave to cool for 10 minutes.
- Use a small cookie cutter to cut out rounds of the rice. Move to a wire rack to cool before serving with cream cheese or peanut butter.

Mini pancakes with fruit

Makes 8 portions and takes 40 minutes.

The more pancakes the better! These are great for feeding the family at breakfast, so why not put out a spread of toppings for everyone to choose from?

2 Golden Delicious apples, peeled, cored and sliced

2 tbsp pure apple juice

1 tsp honey

75 g / 2 ½ oz / ½ cup wholewheat flour, sifted

75 g / 2 ½ oz / ½ cup plain (all-purpose) flour, sifted

1 ½ tsp baking powder

250 ml / 9 fl. oz / 1 cup milk

1 tbsp vegetable oil

1 tbsp water

non-fat cooking spray

icing (confectioners') sugar, to garnish (optional)

- Combine the apples, apple juice and honey in a small saucepan. Cook over a low heat, stirring occasionally, until the slices are soft but not mushy. Remove from the heat.
- Combine the flours and baking powder in a large mixing bowl. Slowly whisk in the milk, oil and water until the batter comes together.
- Spray a small crêpe or pancake pan with non-fat cooking spray and heat over a medium heat until hot. Drop small ladles of the batter onto the pan and cook for 1–2 minutes until set. Flip and cook for a further minute or so until golden underneath. Slide onto a plate.
- Repeat with the remaining batter until all the pancakes are cooked.
- Stack the pancakes on plates and top with the apples and a slight dusting of icing sugar if desired.

NOTE: Not suitable for babies under 12 months.

Hummus and veg sticks

Makes 8 portions and takes 15 minutes.

Veg sticks are the perfect finger food for growing children and will help in their development over the weaning period. The creamy consistency of hummus is ideal for babies and will become a go-to recipe when you are in need of a quick fix.

200 g / 7 oz / 1 cup canned chickpeas, drained

½ clove garlic, minced

a pinch ground cumin

2 tbsp lemon juice

1 tbsp olive oil

1 cucumber, cut into sticks

2 carrots, peeled and cut into sticks

2 sticks celery, peeled and cut into sticks

• Combine the chickpeas, garlic, cumin, lemon juice, olive oil and 2 tbsp of warm water in a food processor. Blend until smooth and creamy, scraping down the sides as necessary.

• Spoon into a bowl and serve with the vegetables sticks.

Avocado dip and toasted pitta

Makes 8 portions and takes 15 minutes.

Avocados make a great dip because of their creamy texture and nutrient-packed content. They're full of 'good fats' that babies need in their diet to support physical and brain development. Prepare plenty of this zingy avocado dip, because it's a staple for the whole family!

1 large, ripe avocado, pitted and chopped

2 tbsp low-fat Greek yogurt

1 tbsp lemon juice

1 tbsp olive oil

¼ tsp dried oregano

2 pitta breads, plain or wholemeal

• Combine the avocado, yogurt, lemon juice, olive oil and oregano in a small bowl. Mash well until creamy.

• Lightly toast the pitta breads under a hot grill. Cut into strips and allow to cool slightly, then serve alongside the avocado dip.

Malt loaf slices

Makes 1 small loaf and takes 1 hour.

This sticky malt loaf is so tasty that you'll want to keep it all to yourself! Even at this stage, you'll still be introducing new and exciting flavours to your baby's diet, and it's a good idea to start giving him foods that the rest of the family are eating.

80 ml / 3 fl. oz / ⅓ cup hot black tea

85 g / 3 oz / ½ cup malt extract

55 g / 2 oz / ¼ cup soft brown sugar

75 g / 2 ½ oz / ½ cup mixed dried fruits

1 large egg, beaten

150 g / 5 oz / 1 cup plain (all-purpose) flour

½ tsp baking powder

¼ tsp bicarbonate of (baking) soda

butter, to serve

- Preheat the oven to 160°C (140°C fan) / 300F / gas 2. Grease and line a 450 g / 1 lb loaf tin with greaseproof paper.
- Combine the tea, malt extract, sugar and dried fruits in a mixing bowl, stirring well. Add the eggs and beat well, then fold through the flour, baking powder and bicarbonate of soda until combined.
- Scrape into the prepared loaf tin and bake for 40–50 minutes until firm and risen. Remove to a wire rack to cool. Slice and serve with butter if desired.

Blueberry bread and butter

Makes 1 small loaf and takes 1 hour 30 minutes.

Blueberries are fantastic ingredients in breads and muffins, because they add little bursts of intense flavour that babies love. He will now be accustomed to fruit pieces and finger foods, so these bread slices should be no trouble for your little trouper!

50 g / 1 ¾ oz / ¼ cup unsalted butter, melted

90 g / 3 oz / ½ cup brown sugar

1 tbsp lemon juice

1 medium eggs

110 g / 4 oz / ⅓ cup plain (all-purpose) flour

½ tsp baking powder

60 ml / 2 fl. oz / ¼ cup semi-skimmed milk

100 g / 3 ½ oz / ⅔ cup blueberries, washed

butter, for serving

- Preheat the oven to 180°C (160°C fan) / 350F / gas 4. Grease and line a 450 g / 1 lb loaf tin with greaseproof paper.
- Beat together the butter, sugar, lemon juice and eggs in a mixing bowl. Combine the flour and baking powder separately, then stir into the egg mixture along with the milk. Fold through the blueberries.
- Spoon into the lined tin and bake for 60–70 minutes until golden on top and a toothpick inserted near the centre comes out clean. Remove to a wire rack to cool. Slice and serve with butter.

Summer vegetable stew

Makes 8 portions and takes 30 minutes.

There are plenty of flavours in this chunky stew that your baby will now be familiar with, and it's packed with soft veg that he'll easily be able to chew and digest. Make plenty and freeze some for another night, or serve with crusty bread for the rest of the house.

1 tbsp olive oil

1 onion, diced

1 clove garlic, minced

1 courgette (zucchini), diced

1 aubergine (eggplant), diced

200 g / 7 oz / 1 cup canned chopped
    tomatoes

100 g / 3 ½ oz / ½ cup canned
    chickpeas

100 ml / 3 ½ fl. oz / ½ cup low-sodium
    vegetable stock

couscous, to serve

- Heat the olive oil in a saucepan set over a medium heat until hot. Add the onion, garlic, courgette and aubergine, then sweat for 5–6 minutes until softened.
- Add the chopped tomatoes, chickpeas and stock, stirring well. Cook until simmering, then cover and cook over a low heat for 20 minutes until the chickpeas are tender. Mash roughly with a fork.
- Serve warm with couscous.

Chicken and vegetable couscous

Makes 8 portions and takes 45 minutes.

There are loads of ingredients in this dish that are full of good nutrients, including hearty vegetables, protein-packed meat and healthy grains. Combined, they make a delicious dish for the whole family.

1 tbsp olive oil

1 courgette (zucchini), diced

1 onion, diced

1 clove garlic, minced

200 g / 7 oz / 1 cup canned chickpeas,
    drained

2 small, skinless chicken breasts,
    sliced

2 small tomatoes, diced

a pinch of pepper

175 g / 6 oz / 1 cup couscous

500 ml / 18 fl. oz / 2 cups low-sodium
    chicken stock

- Heat the olive oil in a small casserole dish or saucepan set over a medium heat until hot. Add the courgette, onion and garlic, then sweat for 4–5 minutes until softened.
- Add the chickpeas, chicken, tomatoes and 100 ml / 3 ½ fl. oz / ½ cup of water. Stir well, cook until simmering, then cover and cook over a low heat for 20 minutes. Season to taste with a little pepper. Mash the chickpeas roughly with a fork. The stew can be blended in a food processor for children younger than 12 months.
- Place the couscous in a heatproof bowl. Cover with the stock, stir once and cover well. Leave for 10–15 minutes until the couscous has absorbed the stock. Fluff with a fork and serve with the chicken stew in bowls.

Salmon and corn fishcakes

❄ *Makes 8 portions and takes 1 hour.*

Fishcakes take a while to prepare but they are well worth the effort! The key with time-consuming dishes is to ensure you're not simply feeding your baby for one night. Make it a dish for everyone, or make enough to freeze for another occasion.

2 medium, floury potatoes, peeled and diced

300 g / 11 oz / 2 cups skinless salmon fillet, pin-boned and diced

500 ml / 18 fl. oz / 2 cups semi-skimmed milk

150 g / 5 oz / 1 cup canned sweetcorn, drained

1 spring onion (scallion), diced

1–2 tbsp cornflour (cornstarch)

175 g / 6 oz / 1 ½ cups golden breadcrumbs

- Cook the potato in a large saucepan of salted, boiling water for 18–22 minutes until tender to the point of a knife. Drain well and leave to steam dry to one side.
- Combine the salmon, milk and sweetcorn in a saucepan. Bring to a simmer and poach the salmon for 6–8 minutes until cooked through. Drain well, reserving the cooking liquid.
- Mash the potato with the salmon, sweetcorn, spring onion, cornflour and some of the cooking liquid to loosen the mixture if necessary.
- Shape into eight patties and coat in the breadcrumbs, then cover and chill in the fridge. Preheat the oven to 180°C (160°C fan) / 350F / gas 4.
- Arrange the fishcakes on a baking tray. Bake for 22–25 minutes until golden and crisp, turning after 15 minutes.

White fish and leek patties

❄ *Makes 8 portions and takes 1 hour.*

These patties are a fun way to get fish into your baby's diet – they're finger foods that are packed with various nutrients, including omega 3 from the fish, carbohydrates from the potato and healthy vitamins from the leek.

750 ml / 26 fl. oz / 3 cups semi-skimmed milk

2 medium, floury potatoes, peeled and diced

300 g / 11 oz / 2 cups skinless cod fillet, pin-boned and diced

½ small leek, sliced and washed

1–2 tbsp cornflour (cornstarch)

175 g / 6 oz / 1 ½ cups golden breadcrumbs

a little pepper

- Warm the milk in a saucepan set over a moderate heat. Add the potato and simmer for 10 minutes. Add the cod, cover with a lid and simmer over a reduced heat for 5–7 minutes.
- Strain the mixture and mash with the leek, cornflour and a pinch of pepper. Let the mixture cool slightly before shaping into eight patties. Coat in the breadcrumbs and arrange on a baking tray.
- Preheat the oven to 180°C (160°C fan) / 350F / gas 4.
- Bake the patties for 22–25 minutes until golden and crisp, turning after 15 minutes. Serve with a little ketchup for dipping.

Risotto with peas and courgettes

❄ *Makes 4 portions and takes 35 minutes.*

Risotto is a great meal for babies because of its thick, lumpy texture that requires those now found chewing skills. This healthy option contains flavours that your baby will adapt to quickly,

1 tbsp olive oil

1 small onion, chopped

1 courgette (zucchini), finely chopped

175 g / 6 oz / ¾ cup risotto rice

100 g / 3 ½ oz / ¾ cup frozen peas

50 g / 1 ¾ oz / ½ cup Cheddar cheese, grated

- Heat the oil in a large heavy-based pan, add the onion and fry gently for a few minutes to soften, but not brown. Add the courgettes to the pan and cook for a couple of minutes, then stir in the risotto rice.
- Add 300 ml / 10 fl. oz / 1 ¼ cups boiling water, then stir and cook for a few minutes until the liquid is absorbed. Add another 300 ml / 10 fl. oz / 1 ¼ cups of water and stir occasionally until the liquid is absorbed.
- Add the peas and a final 300 ml / 10 fl. oz / 1 ¼ cups of water, then stir and simmer until the rice is tender and the liquid is almost absorbed. Remove from the heat and stir in the cheese to serve.

Tuna risotto

❄ *Makes 8 portions and takes 35 minutes.*

Canned tuna is an easy way to build fish into your baby's diet and this easy risotto is sure to be popular with the whole family. Start gently with the dill garnish until your baby is used to the distinctive flavour.

1 tbsp olive oil

1 shallot, diced

1 medium carrot, peeled and sliced

1 clove garlic, minced

200 g / 7 oz / 1 cup canned kidney beans, drained

100 g / 3 ½ oz / ⅔ cup canned sweetcorn, drained

200 g / 7 oz / 1 ¼ cups canned tuna steak, drained

85 g / 3 oz / ½ cup short-grain rice

500 ml / 18 fl. oz / 2 cups low-sodium vegetable stock

a little pepper

1 tbsp chopped dill, to garnish

- Heat the oil in a casserole dish or large saucepan set over a medium heat. Add the shallot, carrot and garlic, then sweat for 5 minutes until softened.
- Add the beans, sweetcorn and tuna, stirring well. Stir through the rice and stock and bring the liquid to a simmer.
- Cover with a lid and cook over a low heat for 25–30 minutes, stirring from time to time, until the rice is tender. Season to taste with a little pepper. Serve with a small garnish of dill.

Pasta with home-made pesto

Makes 8 portions and takes 15 minutes.

Pesto is a versatile ingredient that can be used in many dishes, so prepare plenty and store in the fridge for up to a week to save you some time. This dish is really easy and something that the whole family will enjoy.

110 g / 4 oz / ¾ cup sun-dried
    tomatoes, soaked in hot water for
    10 minutes

2 tbsp basil leaves

1 clove garlic, chopped

1 tbsp pine nuts

1 tbsp olive oil

100 g / 3 ½ oz / 2 cups pasta shapes

- Remove the sun-dried tomatoes from the soaking water (reserving the water) and combine with the basil, garlic, pine nuts, olive oil and 2 tbsp of the soaking water in a food processor. Blend until smooth.
- Cook the pasta in a large saucepan of unsalted, boiling water for 6–8 minutes until tender. Drain well and toss with the pesto.

Pasta stars with tomato sauce

Makes 8 portions and takes 20 minutes.

Pasta shapes are a really easy way to make dinner time more exciting, and there are plenty of varieties on the market. This dish is so simple that it'll become one of your staples, and baby will love it, too!

1 tbsp olive oil

½ clove garlic, minced

200 g / 7 oz / 1 cup passata

100 g / 3 ½ oz / 2 cups pasta stars

- Heat the oil in a saucepan set over a medium heat until hot. Add the garlic and sauté for 30 seconds. Stir in the passata and cook until simmering. Reduce the heat to low and cook for 4–5 minutes until slightly thickened.
- Cook the pasta stars in a large saucepan of unsalted boiling water for 6–8 minutes until tender. Drain well and stir into the tomato sauce. Serve warm.

Stage 3 meal planner

	Monday	Tuesday	Wednesday
Wake Up	Milk	Milk	Milk
Breakfast	Mini fruit rolls	Simple scrambled egg	Granola with raspberries
Mid Morning	Hummus and veg sticks	Avocado dip and toasted pitta	Malt loaf slice
Lunch	Chicken and vegetable couscous	Summer vegetable stew	Tuna risotto
Mid Afternoon	Milk	Milk	Milk
Dinner	Pasta with home-made pesto	White fish and leek patties	Chicken and vegetable couscous
Evening	Milk	Milk	Milk

Thursday	Friday	Saturday	Sunday
Milk	Milk	Milk	Milk
Fruity muesli	Mini fruit rolls	Simple scrambled egg	Mini pancakes with fruit
Mini rice cakes	Hummus and veg sticks	Blueberry bread and butter	Mini rice cakes
Risotto with peas and courgettes	Salmon and corn fishcakes	Pasta stars with tomato sauce	Turkey, rice, carrot and broccoli
Milk	Milk	Milk	Milk
Pasta with home-made pesto	Summer vegetable stew	Lamb with lentils	Pasta stars with tomato sauce
Milk	Milk	Milk	Milk

Toddler
Recipes

The main change in your baby's diet after 12 months is the introduction of whole milk. It is no longer essential that your baby has breast milk or infant formula, so your baby will now be dependent on the food she eats and fluids to gain all her nutrients. As your toddler becomes more mobile, her energy requirement will increase, making convenient, healthy snacks a must.

The recipes in this section can be used in conjunction with the stage 3 recipes to form weekly meal plans, although these meals have been selected to be suitable for the whole family to enjoy together. Try some of these healthy snacks yourself and see how your baby responds when she sees you enjoying the same food as her!

Toast with bacon and tomato

Makes 8 portions and takes 15 minutes.

Who can resist bacon at breakfast? This is bound to be a firm favourite with parent and baby alike, so you won't mind if baby doesn't finish his! The various components make brilliant finger foods and it's also a filling way to get his day off to a great start.

4 rashers back bacon

2 vine tomatoes, cored and cut in half horizontally

4 slices wholemeal bread

2 tbsp butter, softened

- Preheat the grill to hot. Grill the bacon and tomato halves for 3–4 minutes, turning occasionally, until the bacon is cooked through.
- Remove from the grill and pat the bacon with kitchen paper. Toast the bread in a toaster or under the grill. Butter the toast and serve with the bacon and tomato on plates.

Waffles with fruit

Makes 8 portions and takes 25 minutes.

Waffles are really easy if you have a waffle iron to hand! These are such crowd-pleasers and taste great with a variety of toppings.

300 g / 11 oz / 2 cups plain (all-purpose) flour

2 tsp baking powder

1 tbsp sugar

¼ tsp salt

½ tsp vanilla extract

2 medium eggs

55 ml / 2 fl. oz / ¼ cup sunflower oil

400 ml / 14 fl. oz / 1 ⅔ cup semi-skimmed milk

non-fat cooking spray

chopped fresh fruit, to serve

- Preheat a waffle iron according to the manufacturer's instructions.
- Mix together the flour, baking powder, sugar and salt in one bowl. Beat together the vanilla, eggs, oil and milk in a mixing jug.
- Combine the wet and dry ingredients, taking care not to over-mix.
- Spray the surface of the iron with non-fat cooking spray. Cook the batter according to the instructions and let the waffles cool on a wire rack before serving with your choice of fresh fruit.

Eggy bread

Makes 4 portions and takes 10 minutes.

This might sound like an indulgent version of toast, but eggs are a nutritious part of baby's diet and provide heaps of important vitamins. Eggy bread isn't just for babies either – why not treat all the family to this delicious breakfast?

4 medium eggs

55 ml / 2 fl. oz / ¼ cup
   semi-skimmed milk

4 slices white bread

2 tbsp butter

- Beat the eggs with the milk in a shallow dish. Dip the bread into the mixture, coating both sides.
- Melt a knob of butter in a frying pan set over a moderate heat until hot. Fry the dipped bread slices for 1–2 minutes on both sides until golden. Repeat using a fresh of knob of butter for each slice. Serve warm.

  NOTE: Not suitable for babies under 12 months.

Egg and soldiers

Makes 4 portions and takes 10–15 minutes.

This easy, nutritious dish is a must. A bright set of egg cups is a great way to engage your baby with his food and toast soldiers can easily be cut into different shapes for added mealtime fun!

4 medium eggs

4 slices white bread

- Cook the eggs in a saucepan of boiling water for 8 minutes. Drain and refresh briefly in cold water.
- Toast the bread in a toaster or under a hot grill. Cut into soldiers and serve with the boiled eggs in egg cups.

  NOTE: Not suitable for babies under 12 months.

Multigrain cereal muffins

Makes 12 muffins and takes 1 hour 30 minutes.

Muffins are a quick, pain-free breakfast that require zero preparation once baked. Being organized is half the battle when you have a baby, so having a stash of these muffins prepared will save you a lot of stress later. Plus, they make delicious snacks!

80 g / 3 oz / 2 cups rolled oats, plus extra for topping

40 g / 1 ½ oz / ¼ cup ground flaxseeds

250 ml / 9 fl. oz / 1 cup buttermilk

110 g / 4 oz / ½ cup butter

80 g / 3 oz / ⅓ cup sugar

1 medium egg

120 g / 4 oz / ¾ cup plain (all-purpose) flour

1 tsp baking powder

½ tsp bicarbonate of (baking) soda

- Mix together the oats, flaxseeds and buttermilk, then set aside for 1 hour.
- Preheat the oven to 180°C (160°C fan) / 350°F / gas 4. Line a 12-hole muffin tin with cases. Beat the butter and sugar in a mixing bowl until light and fluffy. Beat in the egg until blended.
- Sift together the flour, baking powder and bicarbonate of soda. Gently stir into the butter mixture, alternately with the oat mixture.
- Spoon into the paper cases and sprinkle the tops lightly with rolled oats. Bake for 20–25 minutes, until risen and golden. Cool in the tin for 5 minutes, then place on a wire rack to cool completely.

Oatmeal–raisin muffins

Makes 12 muffins and takes 1 hour 30 minutes.

Smaller foods such as raisins are absolutely fine to introduce at this stage in your baby's development. Mixed into these oaty muffins, they'll add a burst of fruity sweetness at breakfast time.

110 g / 4 oz / 2 ¼ cups rolled oats, plus extra for topping

250 ml / 9 fl. oz / 1 cup buttermilk

110 g / 4 oz / ½ cup butter

80 g / 3 oz / ⅓ cup sugar

1 medium egg

120 g / 4 oz / ¾ cup plain (all-purpose) flour

1 tsp baking powder

½ tsp bicarbonate of (baking) soda

75 g / 2 ½ oz / ½ cup raisins

- Mix together the oats and buttermilk, then set aside for 1 hour.
- Preheat the oven to 180°C (160°C fan) / 350°F / gas 4. Line a 12-hole muffin tin with cases. Beat the butter and sugar in a mixing bowl until light and fluffy. Beat in the egg until blended.
- Sift together the flour, baking powder and bicarbonate of soda. Gently stir into the butter mixture, alternately with the oat mixture. Fold in the raisins.
- Spoon into the paper cases and sprinkle the tops lightly with rolled oats. Bake for 20–25 minutes, until risen and golden. Cool in the tin for 5 minutes, then place on a wire rack to cool completely.

Ham and cream cheese sandwiches

Makes 2 sandwiches and takes 10 minutes.

4 slices white or brown bread
40 g / 1 ½ oz / ¼ cup butter

For the filling:
4 slices thick-cut ham
100 g / 3 ½ oz / ½ cup cream cheese

- Cut the crusts off the bread and flatten each slice with a rolling pin.
- Spread the slices with a little butter on one side. Top two slices of bread with the cream cheese and ham, then top with the remaining bread slices.
- Using a butterfly shaped cookie cutter or a stencil, cut shapes out of the sandwiches and arrange on a serving plate.

Pesto and mozzarella sandwiches

Makes 2 sandwiches and takes 10 minutes.

4 slices white or brown bread
40 g / 1 ½ oz / ¼ cup butter

For the filling:
150 g / 5 oz / ¾ cup fresh mozzarella, drained and sliced
100 g / 3 ½ oz / ½ cup basil pesto

- Cut the crusts off the bread and flatten each slice with a rolling pin.
- Spread the slices with a little butter on one side. Top two slices of bread with the mozzarella and pesto, then top with the remaining bread slices.
- Using a butterfly shaped cookie cutter or a stencil, cut shapes out of the sandwiches and arrange on a serving plate.

Top tip

It's fine to use gluten-free bread for these sandwiches, if you need to make a gluten-free version.

If you don't have a butterfly-shaped cookie cutter, it might be a little difficult to create butterfly shapes without ending up with cream cheese filling all over the place! Fun shapes are a great way to engage your child with his food, but simple triangles or soldiers will taste just as good.

Vegi maki rolls

Makes 8 rolls and takes 10 minutes.

These fun rolls are a great lunch box treat! The bright colours and bitesize pieces are sure to make them a popular meal. They're also easy to make batches of for party food.

4 slices wholemeal bread

55 g / 2 oz / ¼ cup butter, softened

100 g / 3 ½ oz / ½ cup sesame seeds

4 large carrots, peeled and grated

1 small cucumber, seeded and cut into batons

- Cut the crusts from the slices of bread, then lightly butter the top side of the bread. Sprinkle evenly with sesame seeds, then roll a rolling pin across their tops to flatten them out and help the seeds stick to the bread.
- Carefully turn the bread over and top with the grated carrots and cucumber batons. Roll into cigar shapes and cut into rolls. Serve immediately or chill until needed.

NOTE: Sesame seeds are not suitable for babies under 12 months if there is a family history of allergies.

Chicken and veg rice paper rolls

Makes 8 rolls and takes 10 minutes.

These wraps are a fantastic way to get valuable veggies and meat into baby's diet, all in one bitesize mouthful! Introducing new flavours, such as soy sauce and rice wine vinegar, with old favourites like carrot and cucumber will help him to accept these new and interesting foods.

1 carrot, peeled and shredded

½ small cucumber, cut into thin strips

50 g / 1 ¾ oz / 1 cup baby spinach, washed

1 tbsp low-sodium soy sauce

1 tbsp rice wine vinegar

8 rice paper wrappers, kept under a damp cloth

2 cooked skinless chicken breasts, cut into strips

- Toss the veggies and spinach with the soy sauce and vinegar. Arrange in the centre of the rice paper rolls and top with strips of chicken in the middle.
- Fold the ends of the paper over on top of the filling and roll into tight rolls. Serve immediately or chill until needed.

Fish fingers and courgettes

Makes 4 portions and takes 25 minutes.

Arranging your baby's food into fun shapes is a great way to engage her with her food. It doesn't always need to be an aeroplane flying into her mouth!

12 frozen fish fingers

1 medium courgette (zucchini), thickly sliced

1 tbsp olive oil

1 small head broccoli, broken into florets

celery to garnish, if desired

- Preheat the oven to 230°C (210°C fan) / 450F / gas 8. Arrange the fish fingers on a large baking tray, spaced apart. Bake for 12–15 minutes until golden and crisp, turning them over halfway through.
- Meanwhile, gently fry the courgette slices in the oil over a medium heat until browned on each side.
- Cook the broccoli in a pan of boiling water for 8–10 minutes until tender.
- Drain the broccoli. Arrange the fishfingers and courgettes into a tractor shape, adding broccoli 'trees' for decoration.
- Add pieces of celery to form the 'cabin' and the 'headlights' if desired.

Spanish omelette

Makes 8 portions and takes 25 minutes.

This versatile dish is great at any time of day, plus if you have any leftovers, you can slice them and keep them chilled until snacktime. This recipe uses potato and onion, but chopped ham, sliced peppers and tomatoes all work equally well

2 tbsp olive oil

450 g / 1 lb / 3 cups new potatoes, thinly sliced

1 small onion, chopped

2 tbsp flat-leaf parsley, chopped

6 medium eggs, beaten

- Preheat the oven to 180°C (160°C fan) / 350F / gas 4. Heat the olive oil in a cast-iron pan set over a medium heat until hot.
- Add the potato and onion to the oil and saute for 4–5 minutes, partially covered, until the potato is tender. Scatter the parsley on top and then pour over the egg.
- Bake for 12–15 minutes until the egg is puffed and golden. Remove from the oven and leave to cool slightly before serving.

Toad in the hole

Makes 8 portions and takes 35-40 minutes.

Hearty dishes like toad in the hole are family-pleasers, and it's fantastic when you can feed the whole family – including baby – with one simple, delicious meal. Ensure baby's portion is a suitable size and check the temperature of the sausages before letting him loose on his dinner.

215 g / 8 oz / 1 ½ cups plain (all-purpose) flour

3 medium eggs, beaten

375 ml / 13 fl. oz / 1 ½ cups semi-skimmed milk

2 tbsp butter, melted

2 tbsp vegetable oil

8 small good-quality pork sausages

- Preheat the oven to 220°C (200°C fan) / 425F / gas 7.
- Place the flour in a mixing bowl. Make a well in the centre and whisk in the eggs, milk and butter until a batter comes together. Transfer to a jug.
- Grease a large casserole or baking dish with half the oil. Place in the oven to preheat. Meanwhile, heat the remaining oil in a large sauté pan and brown the sausages, in batches if necessary.
- Once the dish in the oven has preheated for at least 10 minutes, carefully remove and add the sausages. Pour over the batter and bake in the oven for 18–22 minutes until the batter is golden and risen.

Bubble and squeak cakes

Makes 8 portions and takes 20-30 minutes.

These little patties are a great take on traditional bubble and squeak. The finger-food size makes them perfect for growing babies, as well as a good way to use up any leftovers.

600 g / 21 oz / 3 cups mashed potato, leftover

1 medium carrot, grated

½ small cabbage, shredded

2 spring onions (scallions), chopped

3 tbsp cornflour (cornstarch)

3 tbsp sunflower oil

- Preheat the oven to 180°C (160°C fan) / 350F / gas 4.
- Mash together the potato, carrot, cabbage and spring onion. Shape into eight small patties and dust in the cornflour, shaking off any excess.
- Heat the oil in a large sauté pan set over a moderate heat until hot. Fry the patties for 2–3 minutes until golden underneath. Flip and transfer the pan to the oven (or place the cakes on a baking tray) to finish cooking for 6–7 minutes.
- Remove from the oven and allow to cool before serving.

Turkey burgers and salad

❄ *Makes 8 portions and takes 40 minutes.*

These burgers are a definite crowd-pleaser! Try minced chicken for a change, or a hearty beef burger topped with cheese. A build-your-own policy is great fun for older kids.

450 g / 16 oz / 3 cups turkey mince

50 g / 1¾ oz / ½ cup white
    breadcrumbs

1 tbsp mayonnaise

2 tbsp sunflower oil

8 small burger buns, split

150 g / 5 oz / 3 cups mixed leaf salad

a little pepper

- Preheat the oven to 200°C (180°C fan) / 400F / gas 6.
- Mix together the turkey mince, breadcrumbs, mayonnaise and a little pepper in a mixing bowl. Shape into eight small patties and arrange on a baking tray, spaced apart.
- Drizzle with sunflower oil, rubbing into both sides. Bake for 18–22 minutes until golden, turning halfway through. Remove from the oven and serve in buns with the salad.

Veggie burgers and salad

❄ *Makes 8 portions and takes 40 minutes.*

A healthy veggie burger is a great way to pack loads of good nutrients into one dish, and it tastes fantastic!

400 g / 14 oz / 2 cups mashed potato

½ courgette (zucchini), grated

50 g / 1 ¾ oz / ½ cup white
    breadcrumbs

1 tbsp mayonnaise

½ tsp paprika

3 tbsp cornflour (cornstarch)

2 tbsp sunflower oil

8 small burger buns, split

150 g / 5 oz / 3 cups mixed leaf salad

a little pepper

- Preheat the oven to 200°C (180°C fan) / 400F / gas 6.
- Mix together the mashed potato, courgette, breadcrumbs, mayonnaise, paprika and a little pepper in a mixing bowl. Shape into eight small patties and dust with cornflour, shaking off the excess.
- Arrange on a baking tray, spaced apart, then drizzle with sunflower oil, rubbing into both sides. Bake for 18–22 minutes until golden, turning halfway through. Remove from the oven and serve in buns with the salad.

Pasta nests with bacon & mushrooms

❄ *Makes 8 portions and takes 40 minutes.*

2 tbsp butter, melted

400 g / 14 oz spaghetti

100 g / 3 ½ oz / ½ cup pancetta, diced

75 g / 2 ½ oz / 1 cup button
mushrooms, diced

2 tbsp Parmesan, grated

a little pepper

- Preheat the oven to 190°C (170°C fan) / 375F / gas 5.
  Grease 8 holes of a muffin tin with the butter and chill the tin.
- Cook the spaghetti in a large saucepan of boiling water for
  8–10 minutes until tender. Drain well and refresh in cold water.
- Drain again and pat dry. Line the greased holes of the muffin tin
  with the spaghetti, twirling to fit. Top with the diced pancetta and
  mushrooms. Sprinkle over the Parmesan and a little seasoning,
  then bake for 10–15 minutes until crisp on top.

Pasta with mixed vegetables

Makes 8 portions and takes 20 minutes.

100 g / 3 ½ oz / 2 cups pasta shapes

50 g / 2 oz / ¼ cup broccoli florets

50 g / 2 oz / ¼ cup cauliflower florets

50 g / 2 oz / ¼ cup courgette (zucchini),
cut into sticks

50 g / 2 oz / ¼ cup red pepper, cut into
strips

50 g / 2 oz / ¼ cup carrot, cut into
matchsticks

50 g / 2 oz / ¼ cup sweetcorn, drained

a small knob of butter, to serve

- Cook the pasta shapes and vegetables in a large saucepan of boiling
  water for 8–10 minutes until tender.
- Drain the pasta and vegetables and toss with a little butter.
- Serve warm or cover and chill to use as a pasta salad.

Top tip

While it's super easy to pick up a packet or jar of pasta sauce, it's
far more nutritious to make your own and might even save you some
pennies. Many shop-bought products contain high levels of hidden salt
and sugar, so making your own also means that you can keep an eye on
your and your baby's intake.

Pasta is a really great dish when you're stuck for ideas, so adding a
few simple sauces to your repertoire will ensure that you'll always have
something healthy to feed the family. Dried pasta is a must for your
kitchen cupboard.

Baby burrito

Makes 8 portions and takes 15 minutes.

Finger food for all the family! Burritos are great for getting the family together, as well as for letting your little one feel like he can join in. At this stage in their development, toddlers mimic what's going on around them, so these wraps are a good way to make him feel involved.

1 tbsp olive oil

½ red onion, chopped

2 tsp taco spice mix

200 g / 7 oz / 1 cup canned red kidney beans, drained and rinsed

300 g / 11 oz / 2 cups cooked long-grain rice

4 large flour tortillas

100 g / 3 ½ oz / 1 cup Cheddar, grated

a little salt and pepper

- Heat the oil in a large saucepan set over a medium heat until hot. Add the onion and taco spice mix and fry for 2 minutes.
- Stir in the beans and rice, cooking for a further 4–5 minutes until warmed through.
- Warm the flour tortillas in a dry frying pan. Fill with the beans and rice and top with the grated cheese. Fold the ends inwards and roll into burritos. Cut in half and serve.

Beans and rice

Makes 8 portions and takes 30 minutes.

Rice is one of the most versatile foods for babies, and can be introduced into their diet early in the weaning process. This simple dish contains a good helping of protein from the kidney beans, while introducing subtle flavours through herbs and gentle spices.

250 g / 9 oz / 1 ½ cups long-grain rice, rinsed and drained

750 ml / 26 fl oz / 3 cups hot water

2 tbsp olive oil

¼ tsp dried oregano

½ tsp paprika

2 cloves garlic, minced

200 g / 7 oz / 1 cup canned red kidney beans, drained and rinsed

100 g / 3 ½ oz / ½ cup canned chopped tomatoes

1 tbsp coriander (cilantro), finely chopped

1 tbsp lime juice

a little pepper

- Combine the rice and water in a saucepan. Cook over a moderate heat until boiling, then cover and cook over a reduced heat for 15–20 minutes until tender. Remove from the heat and set to one side, covered.
- Heat the olive oil in a large saucepan set over a medium heat until hot. Add the oregano, paprika and garlic, frying for 30 seconds. Add the beans and tomato, stirring well. Fluff the rice with a fork and add to the pan.
- Continue to cook over a medium heat until the rice starts to dry out a little. Season to taste with coriander, lime juice and pepper before serving.

Fruit kebabs and chocolate

Makes 8 portions and takes 10 minutes.

The perfect combination of healthy fruits and lovely, sticky chocolate! Babies love sweet foods, and fruit is the best way to give her a sweet fix that's full of nutritional goodness. A drizzle of chocolate over these fruity kebabs is a wonderful treat that everyone can indulge in.

1 kiwi, peeled

2 thick slices fresh pineapple,
  core removed

2 thick slices cantaloupe melon,
  seeds removed

1 thick slice watermelon,
  seeds removed

75 g / 2 ½ oz / ½ cup milk chocolate,
  broken into squares

- Cut the kiwi into quarters, then cut each piece in half to make eight pieces. Cut each pineapple slice into twelve.
- Cut each cantaloupe melon slice into 6 and cut the watermelon slice into twelve.
- Thread alternate pieces of kiwi, pineapple, cantaloupe and watermelon slices onto eight lolly sticks.
- Melt the chocolate in the microwave on medium for 1 minute. Stir until just melted. Drizzle the chocolate over the fruit kebabs.

Fruit kebabs with mint and lime

Makes 8 portions and takes 10 minutes.

Who said that baby food had to be boring?! These zingy fruit kebabs prove that it can be flavourful, healthy and fun. She'll be getting a handful of vital vitamins that are essential for development and growth, while enjoying a range of bold flavours and new textures.

1 kiwi, peeled

2 thick slices fresh pineapple,
  core removed

2 thick slices cantaloupe melon,
  seeds removed

1 thick slice watermelon,
  seeds removed

agave nectar, to drizzle

a squeeze of lime juice

handful mint, chopped

- Cut the kiwi into quarters, then cut each piece in half to make eight pieces. Cut each pineapple slice into twelve.
- Cut each cantaloupe melon slice into 6 and cut the watermelon slice into twelve.
- Thread alternate pieces of kiwi, pineapple, cantaloupe and watermelon slices onto eight lolly sticks.
- Drizzle the agave nectar evenly over the kebabs, followed by a squeeze of lime juice and a garnish of fresh mint.

Frozen blueberry yogurt

❄ Makes 8 portions and takes 30 minutes plus chilling time.

450 g / 16 oz / 2 cups vanilla yogurt

125 ml / 4 ½ fl. oz / ½ cup whole milk

55 g / 2 oz / ¼ cup caster (superfine) sugar

300 g / 11 oz / 2 cups frozen blueberries, thawed

150 g / 5 oz / 1 cup fresh blueberries

- Combine the yogurt, milk and sugar in a large mixing bowl, stirring until sugar dissolves.
- Place the frozen blueberries in a food processor and process until smooth. Strain the purée through a fine sieve into the mixing bowl of yogurt. Stir well.
- Pour the mixture into a freezer-safe dish, topping with the fresh blueberries. Freeze for 1–1 ½ hours until firm.

Frozen raspberry yogurt

❄ Makes 8 portions and takes 30 minutes plus chilling time.

450 g / 16 oz / 2 cups vanilla yogurt

125 ml / 4 ½ fl. oz / ½ cup whole milk

55 g / 2 oz / ¼ cup caster (superfine) sugar

300 g / 11 oz / 2 cups frozen raspberries, thawed

150 g / 5 oz / 1 cup fresh raspberries

- Combine the yogurt, milk and sugar in a large mixing bowl, stirring until sugar dissolves.
- Place the frozen raspberries in a food processor and process until smooth. Strain the purée through a fine sieve into the mixing bowl of yogurt. Stir well.
- Pour the mixture into a freezer-safe dish, topping with the fresh raspberries. Freeze for 1–1 ½ hours until firm

Top tip

Frozen yogurt is a popular alternative to ice cream and is often considered to be healthier.

If you want to add an extra sweet treat to your frozen yogurt, fold through 75 g / 2 ½ oz / ½ cup white chocolate chips when mixing the fruit purée with the yogurt mixture. A small portion is absolutely fine for baby as a nice treat, and you can guarantee she won't be the only one who loves this dessert!

White chocolate popcorn cakes

Makes 20 slices (approx.) and takes 20 minutes.

These tasty treats are perfect party treats or occasional snacks. Kids will love the combination of crunchy and squidgy textures, along with their favourite sweet flavours and fun sprinkles.

40 g / 1 ½ oz / 4 cups popcorn, popped

375 g / 13 oz / 2 ½ cups white chocolate

100 g / 3 ½ oz / 2 cups mini marshmallows

2–3 tbsp sugar sprinkles

- Line a 30 cm x 23 cm (12 in x 9 in) baking tin with non-stick baking paper. Put the popcorn into a mixing bowl.
- Melt the chocolate in a heatproof bowl over a saucepan of simmering water. Remove from the heat and pour over the popcorn.
- Stir in the marshmallows and press into the tin. Sprinkle with sugar sprinkles and leave to set.

Mini cheesecakes

Makes 8 portions and takes 1 hour 10 minutes + chilling time.

This dessert is a great way to introduce your little one to more sophisticated flavours and textures – and the best part is, you can enjoy it, too! Individual cheesecakes are ideal for toddler-sized mouthfuls, but this recipe is suitable for every sweet tooth!

150 g / 5 oz / 1 cup digestive (graham cracker) biscuits, pulsed into fine crumbs

50 g / 1 ¾ oz / ¼ cup unsalted butter, melted

400 g / 14 oz / 2 cups cream cheese

110 g / 4 oz / ½ cup caster (superfine) sugar

1 tbsp cornflour (cornstarch)

1 tbsp vanilla extract

1 tbsp lemon juice

2 large eggs

1 large egg yolk

120 g / 4 oz / ½ cup sour cream

- Preheat the oven to 150°C (130°C fan) / 300F / gas 2. Combine the biscuits and melted butter until they resemble wet sand, then press into eight mini cheesecake moulds.
- Beat the cream cheese in a mixing bowl until smooth and creamy. Add the caster sugar and the cornflour and mix again for 1 minute.
- Add the vanilla extract, lemon juice, eggs and egg yolk, one at a time, beating well between additions. Add the sour cream and mix again until smooth.
- Pour on top of the biscuit base in the moulds and arrange in a roasting tray. Half-fill the roasting tray with boiling water and place the tray in the oven.
- Bake the cheesecakes for 40–50 minutes; test with a wooden toothpick, if it comes out clean, the cheesecakes are ready. Remove from the oven and chill for at least 3 hours before serving.

Oat and honey biscuits

Makes 12 biscuits and takes 30 minutes.

At this stage in your baby's development, he'll be able to start eating honey (provided he is more than one year old). These yummy biscuits combine the nutritious qualities of oats with the sticky sweetness of honey, to create an after-dinner treat that will please the whole family.

120 g / 4 oz / ½ cup butter

2 tbsp honey

1 tsp bicarbonate of (baking) soda

120 g / 4 oz / ½ cup soft brown sugar

120 g / 4 oz / ¾ cup plain (all-purpose) flour

120 g / 4 oz / 3 cups rolled oats

- Preheat the oven to 180°C (160°C fan) / 350F / gas 4. Line 2 baking trays with greaseproof paper.
- Melt the butter and honey in a saucepan set over a low heat. Remove from the heat and stir in the bicarbonate of soda.
- Place the sugar, flour and oats into a mixing bowl. Add the honey mixture, stir and leave to cool slightly. Drop spoonfuls of the mixture, spaced apart, onto the baking trays.
- Bake for 12–15 minutes until golden. Cool on the baking trays for 3 minutes, then place on a wire rack to cool completely.

Potato cakes

Makes 8 portions and takes 25 minutes.

These simple potato cakes provide a generous helping of carbohydrates, and the cheese adds the required fats for your baby's balanced diet. They're great as an afternoon snack, but would work just as well as part of a filling breakfast.

400 g / 14 oz / 2 cups mashed potato

50 g / 1 ¾ oz / ⅓ cup plain (all-purpose) flour

1 medium egg, beaten

50 g / 1 ¾ oz / ½ cup Cheddar, grated

2–3 tbsp sunflower oil

a little pepper

- Mash together the potato, 2 tbsp flour, egg, cheese and a little pepper.
- Shape into eight small patties and dust in the remaining flour, shaking off the excess.
- Heat the oil in a large sauté pan set over a medium heat until hot. Fry the patties, in batches if necessary, for 2–3 minutes until golden underneath.
- Flip and cook for a further 3–4 minutes until golden all over. Drain on kitchen paper and leave to cool before serving.

Strawberry lollies

 *Makes 8 lollies and takes 15 minutes plus chilling time.*

These fun, fruity lollies are the perfect summer treat, but they also have nutritional value. Containing fresh fruit and yogurt, they provide a good helping of calcium to help your child build strong bones.

1 tsp vanilla extract

400 g / 14 oz / 2 ⅔ cups strawberries, hulled

60 g / 2 oz / ½ cup icing (confectioners') sugar

220 g / 8 oz / 1 cup full-fat Greek-style yogurt, beaten

- Blend the vanilla extract, strawberries and icing sugar to a smooth purée in a food processor.
- Half-fill eight small lolly moulds with some strawberry purée, top with the Greek-style yogurt, then more of the strawberry purée. Fit the handles and sticks of the moulds in place.
- Freeze the lollies for at least 4 hours, or preferably overnight. To remove the lollies from the moulds, dip them in hot water for a few seconds and release them. Serve immediately

Blackberry and raspberry lollies

Makes 8 lollies and takes 15 minutes plus chilling time.

Lolly moulds are available in many shops and supermarkets, so it's worth investing in some bright ones for your toddler. She will love helping you make them and it's important to let her feel involved.

1 tsp vanilla extract

200 g / 7 oz / 1 ⅓ cups blackberries

200 g / 7 oz / 1 ½ cups raspberries

60 g / 2 oz / ½ cup icing (confectioners') sugar

220 g / 8 oz / 1 cup full-fat Greek-style yogurt, beaten

- Blend the vanilla extract, blackberries, raspberries and icing sugar to a smooth purée in a food processor.
- Half-fill eight small lolly moulds with some berry purée, top with the Greek-style yogurt, then more of the berry purée. Fit the handles and sticks of the moulds in place.
- Freeze the lollies for at least 4 hours, or preferably overnight. To remove the lollies from the moulds, dip them in hot water for a few seconds and release them. Serve immediately.

Toddler meal planner

	Monday	Tuesday	Wednesday
Wake Up	Milk	Milk	Milk
Breakfast	Waffles with fruit	Egg and soldiers	Multigrain cereal muffin
Mid Morning	Hummus and veg sticks	Blackberry and raspberry lolly	Oat and honey biscuits
Lunch	Baby burrito	Vegi maki rolls	Ham and cream cheese sandwiches
Dessert (Optional)	Frozen raspberry yogurt	White chocolate popcorn cakes	Fruit kebabs and chocolate
Mid Afternoon	Malt loaf slice	Avocado dip and toasted pitta	Hummus and veg sticks
Dinner	Turkey burger and salad	Pasta nests with bacon and mushrooms	Fish fingers and courgettes
Evening	Milk	Milk	Milk

Thursday	Friday	Saturday	Sunday
Milk	Milk	Milk	Milk
Waffles with fruit	Eggy bread	Oatmeal–raisin muffin	Toast with bacon and tomato
Blueberry bread and butter	Mini rice cakes	Potato cakes	Blueberry bread and butter
Pasta with mixed vegetables	Chicken and veg rice paper rolls	Salmon and corn fishcakes	Pesto and mozzarella sandwiches
Strawberry lolly	Mini cheesecake	Frozen blueberry yogurt	Fruit kebabs with mint and lime
Mini rice cakes	Malt loaf slice	Strawberry lolly	Avocado dip and toasted pitta
Beans and rice	Veggie burger and salad	Toad in the hole	Bubble and squeak cakes
Milk	Milk	Milk	Milk

A good start

Nothing goes exactly to plan where kids are concerned, but if you follow a few simple guidelines, you really can't go too wrong when it comes to weaning and feeding. The advice, tips and menus in this book are based on my experience as a mum, combined with my knowledge as a doctor. I have tried not to preach, as I know how utterly patronizing it is to tell people how to bring up their kids. I've attempted to cut through jargon and put a few untruths to bed by simply telling it how it is, warts and all!

Being a parent is one of the most rewarding yet nerve-wracking roles in life. There isn't a day goes by that by you don't question what you are doing for your children. Some days you even question why you ever had children in the first place. It's completely normal. You can go through a whole host of emotions, ranging from joy to anger, in the space of one single meal. It may sound clichéd but it really is a roller coaster. Each individual child is completely different, even in the same family. Don't set any expectations or specific goals. No two journeys from liquid to solid are the same, so ultimately there are no rules. What I have tried to set out are some simple steps so you and your child can go on this journey of discovery together. It shouldn't be seen as a task but more like an adventure, a taste sensation. I want you to relish it, not recoil at prepping yet another purée or mashed potato! If you enjoy it, the little ones are more likely to embrace it and enjoy it too.

They say that an army marches on its stomach. By giving your little soldiers the best of everything where food is concerned you can help them become the best that they can be. By 'best' I don't mean expensive, shop-bought organic or complex foods,

I mean carefully considered food choices, food fit for all the family. The family that sits at the table together reaps the benefits for now and for the future. You can foster healthy habits from a very young age, so don't underestimate the importance of leading by example.

I made some cracking mistakes with my daughter; I'm still making them. But in doing so I learned a whole lot more, some of which I hope you can take from this book. As for the recipes, they are ultra-simple, and even with my remedial culinary skills I found them fairly straightforward. Keep in mind that even if the food ends up on the floor or splatted all over your best frock, this is yet another baby step you have taken towards mastering baby and toddler meals. Remember, it's not a race, but if it was, it would be a marathon not a sprint. Graduate through each step carefully but confidently, savouring the experience as you go. This only happens once in your child's life so don't get so bogged down in the detail that you miss the moment. When it's gone, it's gone. It might not seem like it when you are knee deep in mush and mess, but you will be wishing your time back again when it goes. Enjoy it!

Recipe index

PICTURE CREDITS

2–3 Barbara Peacock / Getty Images
20 Marina Raith / Getty Images

4, 8, 15, 17, 23, 24, 26, 28–29, 46–47, 68–69,
   90–91, 107, 124 iStock / Getty Images

6 Louise Young

13 Thinkstock / Getty Images

All other images: Stockfood